SRA Imagine It!

Skills Practice

Annotated Teacher's Edition

**Level 1
Book 2**

McGraw Hill SRA

Columbus, OH

SRAonline.com

 SRA

Send all inquiries to this address:
SRA/McGraw-Hill
4400 Easton Commons
Columbus, OH 43219-61888

ISBN: 978-0-07-610489-5
MHID: 0-07-610489-3

4 5 6 7 8 9 QDB 13 12

The McGraw·Hill Companies

Table of Contents

Unit 7 I Think I Can

Unit 8 Away We Grow!

Unit 9 Home, Sweet Home

Unit 10 I Am Brave

Name _____ **Date** _____

Sounds and Spellings

OW

Practice **Write the words and sentence in the spaces provided. Write a rhyming word to finish the last sentence.**

how how   now now

Take a towel to the shower.

Take a towel to the shower.

A cow that was <u>brown</u> went to the town .

Apply   **Write the word described by each picture.**

| cat   cow   crow | shower   tower   flower |

cow

flower

Dictation

how   now

clown   crowd

We drove downtown.

Name _____ Date _____

Writing a Make-Believe Story

Think Audience: **Who** will read your story?
Possible Answer a friend, my parents

Purpose: **What** do you want your make-believe story to do?
Possible Answer Tell about
something that is not real

Prewriting **Plan your make-believe story using the story map below.**

Who is the main character?

↓

What is your main character's problem? Do any other characters help or cause the problem?

↓

How does your character solve his or her problem?

Revising **Use this checklist to revise your make-believe story.**

☐ Is the problem presented at the beginning and a solution at the end of the story?

☐ Did you add descriptive details or dialogue?

☐ Did you revise your story with a partner?

Editing/Proofreading **Use this checklist to correct mistakes.**

☐ Are all words spelled correctly?

☐ Did you use correct capitalization and punctuation?

☐ Do quotation marks appear before and after all dialogue phrases?

Publishing **Use this checklist to get your report ready to share.**

☐ Copy your story on a clean sheet of paper.

☐ Draw illustrations to go with your story.

☐ Present your story to the class in a creative way.

Name _____   **Date** _____

Sounds and Spellings

| ou_ |

Practice   **Write the words and sentence in the spaces provided.**

out <u>out</u>   house <u>house</u>

A mouse ran out.

A mouse ran out.

The cloud is round.

The cloud is round.

Apply | **Write the word that correctly completes each sentence.**

| house | out | flower | found | sound | frown |

1. The clown had a frown on his face.

2. The brown house is big.

3. Amber found her mitten.

4. The player was out at home plate.

5. A rose is Mom's favorite flower.

6. The kids did not make a sound.

Name _____ Date _____

Quotation Marks

Focus

Rule
Quotation marks are used at the beginning and end of the exact words someone says. They show what characters say in a story.

Example
"I want to go to the store," said Mary.

Practice

Read each sentence. Underline the exact words someone says. Circle the name of the speaker.

I. "There's a red starfish clinging to that rock," said (Andy.)

2. (Dad) pointed and said, "Look at all the tiny fish!"

3. "Watch out for that hermit crab!" laughed (Tanya.)

Apply **Read the sentences. Write quotation marks at the beginning and end of the exact words someone says.**

4. "Let's make a sand fort!" said Tanya.

5. Andy asked, "Where can we make it?"

6. "This looks like a good spot," said Tanya.

7. Andy smiled and said, "I'll make the towers."

8. "We work well together," said Tanya.

Name _____ Date _____

Sounds and Spellings Review

Practice **Write the word on the line that correctly names each picture.**

> flour bounce clown
>
> sprouts owls trout

1. bounce

2. trout

3. sprouts

4. clown

5. flour

6. owls

Apply Write the word that best completes each sentence.

flowers   hound

around   outside

7. Murphy is a nice hound .

8. Sometimes he just sits outside on the porch.

9. Then he walks around the yard and smells the flowers .

Dictation

found   cloud

town   now

Joan the clown has a crown.

Name _____ Date _____

Selection Vocabulary

Focus

meadow (med′ · ō) *n.* a grassy field (p. 16)
kite (kīt) *n.* a toy that flies in the sky on a long string (p. 16)

Practice **Circle the correct word that completes the sentence.**

1. Alex's _____ flew high in the sky.
   a. carry   **b.** stop   **c.** (kite)

2. Two cows ate grass in the _____.
   a. (meadow)   **b.** music   **c.** today

Apply **Tell whether the boldfaced definition given for the underlined word in each sentence below makes sense. Circle Yes or No.**

> meadow   kite

3. The <u>meadow</u> was filled with flowers.

running . . . . Yes (No)

4. It is not too windy to fly your <u>kite</u>.

a toy that flies in the sky on a long string. . . . . (Yes) No

5. We ate a picnic lunch in the <u>meadow</u>.

grassy field . . . . (Yes) No

6. Gina's yellow <u>kite</u> looks pretty in the blue sky.

quickly . . . . Yes (No)

Name _____ Date _____

/ow/ spelled *ow* and *ou_*

Focus

Rule	Examples
The /ow/ sound can be spelled *ow* or *ou_*.	town gown ouch slouch

Practice Sort the spelling words under the correct heading.

Word List
1. crown
2. tower
3. pouch
4. outside
5. allow
6. chowder
7. round
8. mouse

Challenge Words
9. flower
10. playground

/ow/ spelled *ow*

1. crown
2. tower
3. allow
4. chowder

/ow/ spelled *ou_*

5. pouch
6. outside
7. round
8. mouse

Apply **Write the spelling word next to its meaning clue.**

9. a small bag to carry things   pouch

10. to permit   allow

11. a structure that is
higher than its surroundings   tower

12. a small rodent with long tail   mouse

Circle the correct spelling for each word.
Write the correct spelling on the line.

13. croun (crown)   crown

14. rownd (round)   round

15. (outside) owtside   outside

16. chouder (chowder)   chowder

Name _____ Date _____

Alphabetical Order

Focus

Rule
Alphabetical order, or **ABC order,** means that a group of words is put in the same order as the letters of the alphabet.

Example
apple   bat   cat   dog

Practice   **Write the following words on the lines in alphabetical order.**

cloud   town   baker   monkey   zipper

1. baker

2. cloud

3. monkey

4. town

5. zipper

Apply **Rewrite each group of words on the lines so that they are in ABC order.**

Group 1

yes

pig

game

Group 2

puzzle

happy

taller

6. game

7. pig

8. yes

9. happy

10. puzzle

11. taller

Name _____ **Date** _____

Sounds and Spellings

kn_

Practice | **Write the words and sentences in the spaces provided.**

knit knit knot knot

I know that knight.

I know that knight.

Sue knows how to knit.

Sue knows how to knit.

Apply **Write the word that best completes each sentence.**

know   knock
knee   knot   knead

1. Please knock on the window.

2. She wondered how to tie a knot.

3. Do you know how to skate?

4. Grandma showed me how to knead the batter.

5. He hurt his knee playing football.

Name _____ **Date** _____

Cause and Effect

What makes an event happen is called the **cause**. The event that happens is the **effect**.

Read each effect. Circle the best cause, either a or b.

1. Jake put ice cubes in a glass.
   a. He wanted to empty the ice tray.
   (b.) He wanted a cold drink of water.

2. Our class went to the cafeteria.
   (a.) It was lunchtime.
   b. We needed practice walking in the hallways.

3. The frog snapped at the fly.
   a. It didn't like bugs.
   (b.) It was hungry.

Apply **Read each effect. Draw a line to match it to its cause.**

4. John ran home from the park.

5. The grass was very tall.

6. Beth bought new shoes.

7. Anna closed all the windows.

8. Pam packed her bags.

9. Men made stacks of lumber.

a. There was a breeze blowing.

b. Her old shoes were too small.

c. They were going to build a house.

d. She was going on a trip.

e. He was late for dinner.

f. No one had mowed it.

Name _____ **Date** _____

Sounds and Spellings

aw

au_

Practice **Write the words and sentences in the spaces provided.**

raw raw   bawl bawl

pause pause

The baby crawls on the lawn.

The baby crawls on the lawn.

Apply **Write the word from the box that completes each sentence.**

I. Paul put milk in the saucer .

| saw |
| saucer |

2. The hawk raised its claw .

| straw |
| claw |

3. Mom made sauce to put over the pasta.

| sauce |
| shawl |

Name _____ Date _____

Writing a Make-Believe Story

Think

Audience: **Who** will read your story?
Possible Answer a friend, my parents

Purpose: **What** do you want your make-believe story to do?
Possible Answer Tell about something that is not real

Prewriting Use the story map below to help plan your make-believe story.

Beginning:
Cosmo and his friends play hide and seek in the ocean.

↓

Middle:
Cosmo gets lost.

↓

End:
A blue whale helps Cosmo get home.

Revising Use the following checklist to revise your make-believe story.

☐ Does your story have a beginning, middle, and end?

☐ Did you describe your story's setting?

☐ Did you use details like description and action words in your story?

Editing/Proofreading Use the following checklist to check your writing for mistakes.

☐ Are all words spelled correctly?

☐ Did you use correct punctuation, including quotation marks?

☐ Did you use singular and plural nouns and pronouns correctly in your story?

Publishing Use this checklist to prepare your story for publication.

☐ Copy your story on a clean sheet of paper.

☐ Use a fun way to present your story like dressing up as a character.

Name _____ **Date** _____

Sounds and Spellings

> **aw** as in w**a**lk and b**all**

Practice **Write the words and sentences in the spaces provided.**

stalk stalk

wall wall

small small

chalk chalk

You should always walk in the hall.

You should always walk in the

hall.

Apply **Circle the correct word that completes each sentence. Write the word on the line.**

1. I need to ___talk___ to my mother.

  (talk) tall

2. Matt and Jeff ___walk___ to the park.

  wall (walk)

Dictation

jaw   drawn

stall   chalk

We played ball on Paul's lawn.

Name _____ Date _____

Singular and Plural Pronouns

Rule
We use **pronouns** to replace nouns and make writing easier and more interesting to read.

Example
<u>Dawn</u> has pretty hair.
She has pretty hair.

Practice **Read the sentence. Look at the picture. Write the correct pronoun on the line.**

| it | they | we | he | him | she | I |

1. I can kick it _____ very far.

2. She _____ is on my team.

3. He _____ is my coach.

Apply **Read each pair of sentences. Write the correct pronoun in the blank.**

she   he   her   them   I

4. My name is Kim.

I _____ am seven years old.

5. Janet likes to paint.

She _____ is an artist.

6. Chad lives next door.

He _____ likes to draw.

7. Janet and Chad are going to an art show.

I am going with them _____.

Name _____ Date _____

Sounds and Spellings

aw as in c**augh**t and th**ough**t

Practice **Write the word on the line that completes each sentence.**

bought   taught   ought
brought   thought

1. Dawn and I think our dog <u>ought</u>
   to have a new doghouse.

2. We <u>thought</u> it would be fun to make it.

3. We <u>bought</u> some wood and nails.

4. Mr. Hon <u>brought</u> over his tools.

5. He <u>taught</u> us how to make the doghouse.

Apply **Read the clues. Write the word in the puzzle.**

thoughtful   caught   fought   daughters

¹f
o
³c a u g h t
u
g
h
⁴t h o u g h t f u l

²d
a
u
g
h
t
e
r
s

Across

3. did catch

4. very kind

Down

1. argued

2. what girls are to their parents

Phonics • *Skills Practice 2*

Name _____ Date _____

/aw/ spelled *au_* and *aw*

Focus

Rule	Examples
The /aw/ sound can be spelled *au_* and *aw*.	law fawn cause

Practice Sort the spelling words under the correct heading.

Word List
1. draw
2. lawn
3. fault
4. auto
5. saw
6. pause
7. awful
8. because

Challenge Words
9. applaud
10. straw

/aw/ spelled *au_*

1. fault

2. auto

3. pause

4. because

/aw/ spelled *aw*

5. draw

6. lawn

7. saw

8. awful

Apply **Circle the correct spelling for each word.**
Write the correct spelling on the line.

9. drau (draw) <u>draw</u>

10. becawse (because) <u>because</u>

11. (lawn) laun <u>lawn</u>

12. auful (awful) <u>awful</u>

Write the spelling word next to its meaning clue.

13. a short break <u>pause</u>

14. mistake <u>fault</u>

15. a car <u>auto</u>

16. pictured with the eye <u>saw</u>

Name _____ Date _____

Sounds and Spellings Review

Practice Write the word that names the picture.

| chalk | crawl | straws | launch | faucet | hawk |

1. straws

2. faucet

3. launch

4. crawl

5. hawk

6. chalk

Apply **Unscramble the words and write the sentence correctly.**

7. dawn. fawn wakes up The at

The fawn wakes up at dawn.

Dictation

caught   bought

saw   sauce

We walked into the store to get

a ball.

Name _____ Date _____

Selection Vocabulary

Focus

dining car (dīn′ · ing kär) *n.* a room on a train where meals are served and eaten (p. 54)

fine (fīn) *adj.* very nice (p. 54)

yards (yärdz) *n.* a place for railroad cars (p. 62)

riddles (rid′ · əlz) *n.* Plural of **riddle:** a question or problem that is hard to solve (p. 73)

Practice **Write the word that completes each sentence.**

1. We ate lunch in the dining car of the train.

2. My brother has a book of jokes and riddles.

3. Maria saw ten blue railroad cars in the yards downtown.

4. It was a fine sunny day.

Apply   **Draw a line to match each word on the left to its definition on the right.**

5. yards

6. dining car

7. fine

8. riddles

a. very nice

b. places for railroad cars

c. questions or problems that are hard to solve

d. a room on a train where meals are served and eaten

Name _____ **Date** _____

Sounds and Spellings

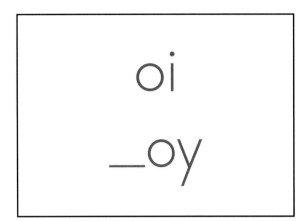

oi

_oy

Practice **Write the words and the sentence on the lines provided.**

noise noise   joy joy

The boy has a nice voice.

The boy has a nice voice.

Apply Complete each sentence with the correct word from the box.

coins toy noise moist point

1. He got a <u>toy</u> at the store.

2. The pencil has a <u>point</u>.

3. She collects <u>coins</u>.

4. The loud <u>noise</u> woke us.

5. The muffin was soft and <u>moist</u>.

Dictation

<u>soil</u>   <u>spoil</u>

<u>toy</u>   <u>enjoy</u>

<u>Place the food in foil.</u>

Name _____ Date _____

Writing a Biography

Think Audience: **Who** will read your biography?
Possible Answer my teacher, my parents

Purpose: **What** do you want your biography to do?
Possible Answer Tell about someone who has done something interesting

Prewriting **Plan your biography using the web below.**

Born February 17, 1963	6 feet 6 inches tall

Michael Jordan

went to University of North Carolina	5 time NBA Most Valuable Player

Revising   **Use the following checklist to revise your biography.**

☐ Did you add details so the reader knows more about the person?

☐ Did you use describing and action words in your biography?

Editing/Proofreading   **Use the following checklist to check your writing for mistakes.**

☐ Did you use correct spelling and punctuation, including quotation marks?

☐ Did you use possessive nouns and pronouns correctly in your writing?

Publishing   **Use this checklist to prepare your biography for publication.**

☐ Copy your biography on a clean sheet of paper.

☐ Use a fun way to present your biography like dressing up as the person, or adding illustrations to your writing.

Name _____ Date _____

Sounds and Spellings Review

Practice **Write the word that names each picture.**

> hoist   toys   oil   coins   cowboys   coil

1. _oil_

2. _coins_

3. _coil_

4. _hoist_

5. _cowboys_

6. _toys_

Apply Write the word on the line that correctly completes each sentence.

enjoyed   voice   choice   annoyed
noise   boiled   loyal   spoiled

7. What was that strange _noise_?

8. Troy must make a _choice_ about which book to read next.

9. Mom threw the _spoiled_ milk in the garbage.

10. Joyce has a nice singing _voice_.

11. Dad _boiled_ some corn for dinner.

12. Roy _enjoyed_ his trip to the beach.

13. The playful puppy _annoyed_ the old dog as it tried to sleep.

14. Leroy and Joy are _loyal_ friends.

Name _____ Date _____

Possessive Pronouns

Focus

Rule	Example
Possessive pronouns take the place of possessive nouns. Possessive pronouns show ownership.	Laura has a blue shirt. It is **her** shirt.

Practice   **Read each sentence. Circle the correct possessive pronoun and write it on the line.**

I. I live in a house on Maple Street.

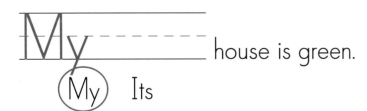

_____ house is green.

(My)   Its

2. Grandma is bringing a puppy.

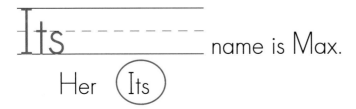

_____ name is Max.

Her   (Its)

Apply

Look at the picture. Read the sentence. Write the possessive noun and what is owned.

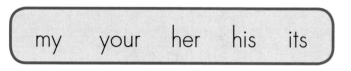

my   your   her   his   its

3. Maria has a book.    her book

4. Ken has a ball.    his ball

5. The cat has a tail.   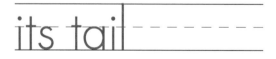 its tail

6. I have a balloon.    my balloon

7. You have an apple.    your apple

Name _____ **Date** _____

Sounds and Spellings

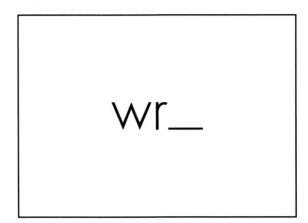

wr_

Practice   **Write the words and the sentence on the lines provided.**

wrist <u>wrist</u>

wrap <u>wrap</u>

Robots wrestle rakes.

<u>Robots wrestle rakes.</u>

Apply **Write the word that goes with each picture.**

write   wrench   wrist

  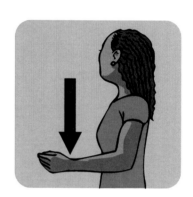

wrench   write   wrist

Dictation

write   wrote

wrist   wreck

We wrote a quick note.

Name _____ Date _____

/oi/ spelled _oy and oi

Focus

Rule	Examples
The /oi/ sound can be spelled _oy and oi.	toy royal boil coil

Word List
1. boy
2. join
3. enjoy
4. loyal
5. spoil
6. voice
7. annoy
8. point

Challenge Words
9. voyage
10. appoint

Practice Sort the spelling words under the correct heading.

/oi/ spelled _oy

1. boy
2. enjoy
3. loyal
4. annoy

/oi/ spelled oi

5. join
6. spoil
7. voice
8. point

Apply **Circle the correct spelling for each word.**
Write the correct spelling on the line.

9. (join) joyn   *join*

10. poynt (point)   *point*

11. (annoy) annoi   *annoy*

12. (loyal) loial   *loyal*

Write the spelling word next to its meaning clue.

13. used to speak   *voice*

14. to damage   *spoil*

15. to like   *enjoy*

16. a male child   *boy*

Name _____ Date _____

Selection Vocabulary

Focus

dew (do͞o) *n.* moisture from the air that forms drops on the grass (p. 90)

silky (sil' · kē) *adj.* soft and smooth (p. 92)

pace (pās) *n.* the speed of walking or running (p. 100)

Practice **Write the word from the word box that completes each sentence.**

1. This morning the grass was wet with dew.

2. The baby went to sleep on a silky blanket.

3. Dave set a fast pace for the runners.

Apply **Write the word from the word box that matches each definition below.**

dew   silky   pace

4. pace _____ the speed of walking or running

5. silky _____ soft and smooth

6. dew _____ moisture from the air that forms drops on the grass

Name _____ **Date** _____

Sounds and Spellings

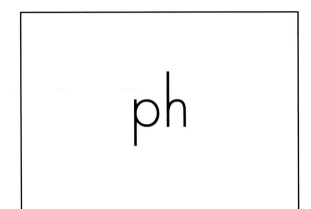

ph

Write the words and the sentence on the lines provided.

photo photo   trophy trophy

Phil's nephew plays the saxophone.

Phil's nephew plays the

saxophone.

Apply **Write the word that names each picture.**

trophy   elephant   dolphin   gopher

trophy

gopher

dolphin

elephant

Name _____ Date _____

Sequence

Focus Telling the events of a story in order is **sequence.** Sequence helps readers better understand what is happening.

Practice **Look at the picture. Place the numbers 1–3 on the lines in front of the sentences to tell the correct order.**

_2_ They walked to the park.

_3_ Then it was time to walk back home.

_1_ Kelsey took the leash off the hook.

Apply **Look at the picture. Read the sentences. Write First, Next, Then, and Finally on the lines to tell the correct order of the story.**

Finally ___ they reach the river where they get a drink of water.

Next ___ the cub wakes up and stretches.

Then ___ the mother tiger leads her cub through the tall grass.

First ___ the mother tiger nudges her sleeping cub.

Name _____ Date _____

Sounds and Spellings

> **er** as in **ear**ly

Practice **Write the word that correctly names each picture.**

> earth   pearl   search   learn   early

1. pearl   2. earth   3. early

4. learn   5. search

Apply **Write the word on the line that correctly completes each sentence.**

research   earns   earth   learning   heard

6. Earl likes learning new things.

7. Earl went to the library to do research.

8. Earl knows that there are many different continents on earth.

9. He has heard about some great places.

10. Earl saves the money he earns so he can take a trip.

Name _____ **Date** _____

Sounds and Spellings

Long ē sound as in donk**ey**

Practice Unscramble the letters to spell the word that correctly names each picture.

1.

    e k y

     key

2.

    e o k c y h

     hockey

3.

    y a l l e

    alley

4.

    n m e o y

    money

5.

    e y j r e s

    jersey

6.

    o h n y e

    honey

Apply **Choose the word that correctly completes each sentence and write it on the line.**

7. Beekeepers gather _honey_.

   valley   honey

8. Carley got a new _volleyball_.

   bee   volleyball

9. Sheep eat grass in the _valley_.

   honey   valley

Dictation

alley   money

phrase   phase

Bert won a trophy for his photo.

Name _____ Date _____

Selection Vocabulary

Focus

stomped (stompt) *v.* Past tense of **stomp**: to walk heavily; to stamp with one foot (p. 117)

rather (rath′ · ûr) *adv.* more gladly (p. 117)

Practice **Review the vocabulary words and definitions from *Winners Never Quit.* Write two sentences that use each of the vocabulary words.**

1. Sentences will vary. Accept ones that correctly

2. use the vocabulary meaning.

Apply   **Write the word from the word box that completes each sentence.**

> rather   stomped

3. Abby <u>stomped</u> around in the tall grass.

4. Would you <u>rather</u> have milk or water to drink?

5. Cara is going now, but Amy would <u>rather</u> go later.

6. Lee <u>stomped</u> on the ground with his foot.

Name _____ Date _____

Expanding Sentences with Describing Words

Rule
You can **expand sentences** and make them more interesting by adding **describing words.** Longer sentences have more information, such as more details and better descriptions of people, places, things, and events.

Look at the picture. Read the sentence. Use the words in the word box to help you write three longer sentences.

plump long orange brown
fluffy pink little black
green leafy big floppy

The bunny eats a carrot.

Answers will vary. Students should write longer sentences using adjectives to describe the bunny.

Apply **Choose one of the lunchboxes. Read the sentence. Write three longer sentences using describing words.**

I have a new lunchbox.

Answers will vary. Students should write longer sentences using adjectives to describe what is on the lunchbox they chose.

Name _____ Date _____

Sounds and Spellings Review

Practice **Name the pictures. Find and circle the word in the puzzle. Write the word on the line.**

p	h	b	g	u	e	a	r	t	h	z
e	e	a	r	t	h	w	o	r	m	s
a	k	a	t	u	r	k	e	y	s	d
r	e	e	a	r	n	i	n	g	s	l
l	y	m	o	n	k	e	y	s	f	e
s	e	o	c	h	i	m	n	e	y	s

Clues

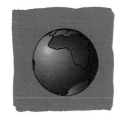

1. monkey   2. earth   3. turkey

4. key   5. pearls   6. chimney

Apply   Read each riddle. Write the word from the word box that correctly answers each riddle.

hockey   learn   earth   donkey

7. I may be math.
I may be reading.
I am what you do every day.
What am I?

8. I am an animal.
I carry things and people.
I look like a horse.
What am I?

9. I am a sport.
Players wear ice skates.
Players move a puck on ice.
What am I?

10. I am a planet.
I am where you live.
I have land and water.
What am I?

Name _____ **Date** _____

/er/ spelled *ear* and /ē/ spelled *_ey*

Focus

Rule
One way to spell the /er/ sound is: **ear.** The vowel sounds of the letters e and *a* are controlled by the letter *r*. One way /ē/ can be spelled is **_ey.**

Examples
yearn   monkey

Word List
1. earth
2. money
3. honey
4. heard
5. donkey
6. search
7. learn
8. valley

Challenge Words
9. unheard
10. volleyball

Practice **Sort the spelling words under the correct heading.**

/er/ spelled *ear*

1. earth
2. heard
3. search
4. learn

/ē/ spelled *_ey*

5. money
6. honey
7. donkey
8. valley

Apply Write the spelling word next to its meaning clue.

9. land surface

10. a horse-like animal

11. a food made by bees

12. low land between hills or mountains

Circle the correct spelling for each word.
Write the correct spelling on the line.

13. (money) mone

14. (heard) hird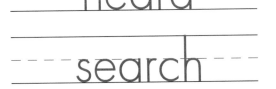

15. (search) serch

16. lern (learn) learn

Name _____ **Date** _____

Interviewing

Focus One way to find out about a person is through an **interview.** If you asked someone questions to find information for your biography, you conducted an interview. Before doing an interview, it is good to prepare a list of questions to ask.

Practice **Who will you interview from your class?**

Possible Answer a friend, my teacher

Below are some questions that might be helpful to ask in an interview.

1. When were you born?

2. Where were you born?

3. Where did you go to school?

4. What is your favorite subject in school?

5. Why is this your favorite subject?

Apply **Conduct an interview with someone in your class. Write questions in the space provided and record the answers from your partner.**

Answers will vary. Accept age appropriate questions and answers.

Use the space below to take more notes while you are conducting your interview.

Name _____ **Date** _____

Timed Writing

Think   **Audience: Who** will read your timed writing?
Possible Answer my teacher

Purpose: What do you want your timed writing to do?
Possible Answer Describe my favorite plant.

Prewriting   **Follow these steps for timed writing.**

1. Read the entire prompt. Circle the directions for writing the paper.

2. Underline each thing you are asked to write about.

3. Reread each reminder.

4. Make notes about what you will write. Spend only a few minutes making notes.

5. Write your paper!

6. Check to make sure you did each reminder.

7. Revise as needed.

Revising Use this checklist to make your timed writing better.

☐ Did you complete each reminder?

☐ Does your writing stay on topic?

☐ Are your sentences clear?

Editing/Proofreading Use this checklist to check your writing.

☐ Did you begin every sentence with a capital letter?

☐ Did you use correct end marks?

☐ Are all words spelled correctly?

Name _____ **Date** _____

Changing Sentences

Focus You can **begin sentences** in different ways to make your writing more interesting.

Practice Read each telling sentence, and then rewrite it so it becomes an asking sentence. The first word of the sentence is given for you.

I. Our class is going on a field trip.

Is our class going on a field trip?

2. We are going to an aquarium.

Where are we going?

3. Some parents will come with us.

Who will come with us?

Apply **Rewrite each telling sentence so that it is an asking sentence.**

Possible Answers

1. Grandpa gave Ted a puppy.

Who gave Ted a puppy?

2. Ted named his new puppy Dusty.

What did Ted name his new puppy?

3. Dusty looks like a black fluffy ball.

What does Dusty look like?

4. Ted takes Dusty for a walk every day after school.

When does Ted take Dusty for a walk?

5. Ted and Dusty are good pals.

Are Ted and Dusty good pals?

Name _____ Date _____

Sounds and Spellings Review

Practice **Draw a line to match the picture to the correct word. Write the word on the line.**

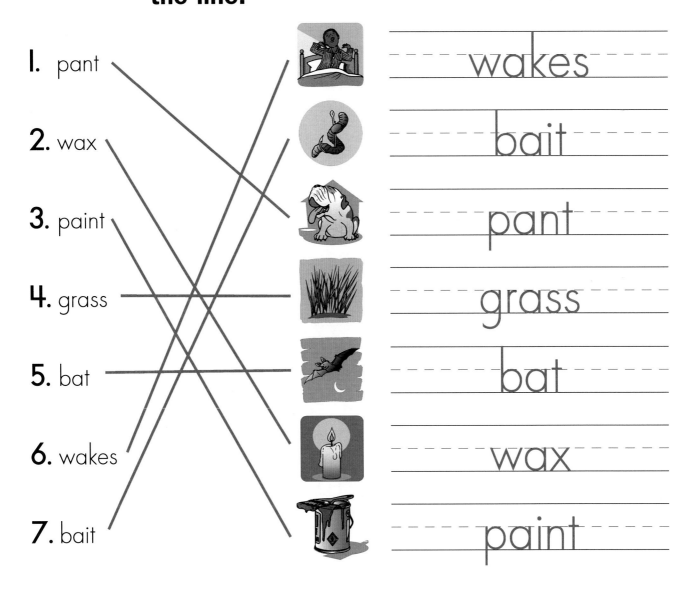

1. pant

2. wax

3. paint

4. grass

5. bat

6. wakes

7. bait

wakes

bait

pant

grass

bat

wax

paint

Apply Write the correct word to complete the sentence. There will be one word that you do not use. Write it at the bottom of the page.

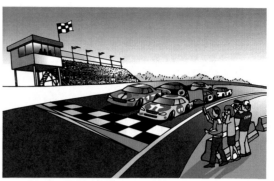

jacket   flat   painted   badge   latch   track   tank

1. Dan had his car painted for the big race.

2. He puts on his racing jacket.

3. He attaches the badge he must wear.

4. Dan makes sure the tank is full of gas.

5. He checks to see that the tires are not flat.

6. Cars begin dashing around the track.

What word did you not use? latch

Name _____ Date _____

Selection Vocabulary

Focus

aside (ə•sīd) *adv.* to one side (page 159)

root (ro͞ot) *n.* part of a plant that grows down into the ground (page 157)

Practice Review the vocabulary words and definitions from "How a Seed Grows." Write a sentence using each vocabulary word. Possible Answers

1. My brother pushed the toy aside when we saw the dog.

2. My dad pulled the plant out by its root.

Apply   **Write the word from the word box that completes each sentence.**

aside   root

1. A ___root___ grows from a seed.

2. The soil is pushed ___aside___ by the growing root.

3. The ___root___ of a plant draws water from the soil.

4. Please move ___aside___ to let others on the bus.

Name _____ Date _____

Long a spelled *a_e* and *ai_*

Focus

Rule	Examples
Long vowels sound like their names. Two ways long a can be spelled are *a_e* and *ai_*.	pave save bait sail

Practice **Sort the spelling words under the correct heading.**

long *a* spelled *a_e*

1. snake
2. tape
3. pale
4. wave

long *a* spelled *ai_*

5. aim
6. wait
7. trail
8. rain

Word List
1. snake
2. aim
3. tape
4. pale
5. wait
6. trail
7. rain
8. wave

Challenge Words
9. trailer
10. snakeskin

Apply **Next to each word, write the spelling word that rhymes.**

9. make   snake

10. bait   wait

11. mail   trail

12. sale   pale

Circle the correct spelling for each word.
Write the correct spelling on the line.

13. rane ⬭(rain)   rain

14. ⬭(aim) ame   aim

15. taip ⬭(tape)   tape

16. waiv ⬭(wave)   wave

Name _____ **Date** _____

Writing a Book Report

Think Audience: **Who** will read your book report?
Possible Answer my friends _____

_____

Purpose: **What** do you want your book report to do?
Possible Answer to tell my
friends about a book I liked

Prewriting **Use the story map to plan your book report.**

Beginning **Possible Answer** Toad wanted to have a garden.

Middle **Possible Answer** Toad tried many things to make his seeds grow.

End **Possible Answer** Toad's seeds started growing.

Revising **Use this checklist to make your book report better.**

☐ Does your paragraph stay on topic?

☐ Did you move words to make your book report clear?

☐ Are there words you can add to tell more about your book?

Editing/Proofreading **Use this checklist to check your book report.**

☐ Did you use pronouns correctly?

☐ Did you use correct end marks?

Publishing **Use this checklist to get your book report ready to share.**

☐ Copy your book report on a clean sheet of paper.

☐ Create a book jacket or illustrate a scene from the book to go with your book report.

Name _____ Date _____

Plural Possessive Pronouns

Focus

Rule	Example
A **plural possessive pronoun** shows ownership. It takes the place of a noun that means more than one.	This cat belongs to us. This cat is **ours.**

Practice **Complete each sentence with the correct plural possessive pronoun.**

> our   ours   their   theirs   your   yours

1. That house across the street belongs to us.

It is __our__ house.

2. Mandy and Rick planted a garden.

__Their__ garden has many plants.

Apply **Read each sentence. Choose the correct possessive pronoun from the box. Write it on the line.**

| mine | your | his | her | their | hers | our |

Grandma has a big attic. There are three old trunks in

__her__ attic. Inside the trunk I found a picture of

Mom and Dad. It was __their__ wedding picture.

These old ice skates would fit Grandma. They must be

__hers__.

Name _____ Date _____

Sounds and Spellings Review

Practice   **Write the word on the line that has the same vowel sound as the picture.**

> spine   might   mit   twine   dries   twin   pickle   knit

1. mit

2. twin

3. pickle

4. knit

5. spine

6. might

7. twine

8. dries

Apply **Write the correct word on the line that completes each sentence.**

| sniff | tries | kitten |
| climb | nibbles | hides |

9. We have a ___kitten___ named Cricket.

10. She likes to ___sniff___ flowers in the garden.

11. She will ___climb___ up tree trunks.

12. Cricket ___nibbles___ her food.

13. She ___tries___ to catch tiny bugs.

14. Cricket ___hides___ under the ivy to take a nap.

Name _____ Date _____

Drawing Conclusions

Focus When you read, use what you learn about the characters and events to **help you better understand the selection.**

Practice **Read the paragraph. Circle the letter that best answers each question.**

Tom pushed the cart as Dad read the list. They had lettuce, celery, and cucumbers in the cart. All they needed were some tomatoes.

1. Where are Tom and Dad?
   a. at the movies
   b. at the market
   c. at the park

2. What are Tom and Dad going to make?
   a. cookies
   b. meatloaf
   c. salad

Apply **Listen as your teacher reads the story. Answer each question with an *X*. Follow the directions under each question.**

It was a hot sunny day. Mike, Sarah, and Jake (laughed) as they walked home together. They stopped and laid their <u>bats,</u> <u>mitts, and caps</u> on the grass. Then they sat down on the grass <u>under a tree.</u> It felt cool in the shade. Sarah (smiled) as she said, "Our team is the best!"

3. How did the children feel?

  ___ sad   <u>X</u> happy   ___ disappointed   ___ angry

Draw a circle around the words that tell you this.

4. What had the children been doing?

  ___ playing soccer   ___ swimming

  <u>X</u> playing baseball   ___ playing tag

Draw two lines under the words that tell you this.

5. Did they win?

  <u>X</u> yes   ___ no

Draw a box around the words that tell you this.

Name _____ **Date** _____

Long i spelled *i_e* and *_y*

Rule
Two ways long i can be spelled are *i_e* and *_y*.

Examples
kite dime pry my

Word List
1. fine
2. time
3. dry
4. shy
5. fly
6. mice
7. by
8. quite

Challenge Words
9. tired
10. crying

Practice **Sort the spelling words under the correct heading.**

long i spelled *i_e*

1. fine
2. time
3. mice
4. quite

long i spelled *_y*

5. dry
6. shy
7. fly
8. by

Apply Below each word, write the spelling words that rhyme.

nine

9. _____fine_____

nice

10. _____mice_____

dime

11. _____time_____

kite

12. _____quite_____

cry

13. _____dry_____

14. _____shy_____

15. _____fly_____

16. _____dry_____

Circle the correct spelling for each word. Write the correct spelling on the line.

17. (quite) quyte _____quite_____

18. (fine) fyne _____fine_____

19. drie (dry) _____dry_____

20. (shy) shie _____shy_____

Spelling · *Skills Practice 2*

Name _____ Date _____

Completing a Web

Focus Filling in a **web** can help you organize information.

Practice Read the words in the middle circle. Read the example in the oval. Add additional examples to complete the web.

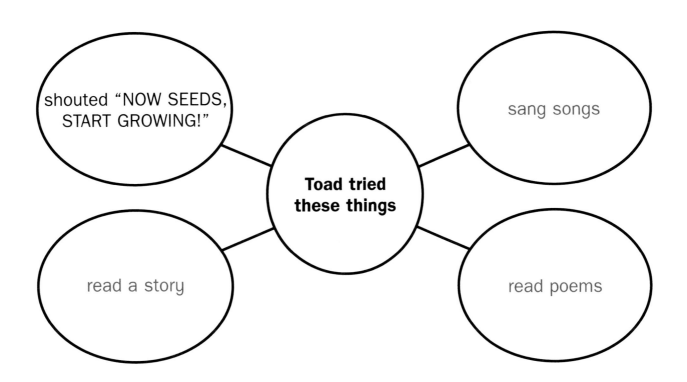

shouted "NOW SEEDS, START GROWING!"

sang songs

Toad tried these things

read a story

read poems

Apply Choose something about plants you are interested in. Write it in the middle circle. Then complete the web with additional information.

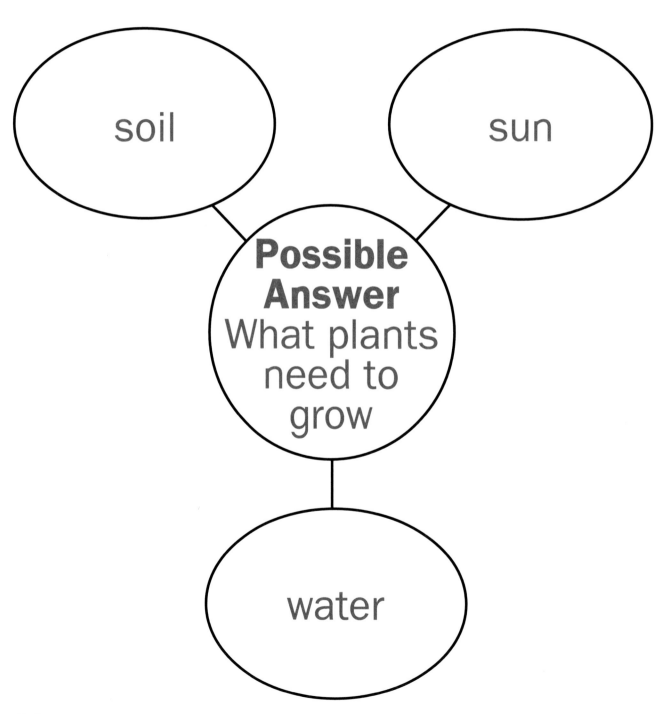

Name _____ **Date** _____

Selection Vocabulary

Focus

flower (flou´•ûr) *n.* colored blossom (page 175)

quite (kwīt) *adv.* very (page 175)

shouted (shout´•ed) *v.* Past tense of **shout**: to call loudly (page 178)

tight (tīt) *adj.* held firmly; secure (page 196)

Practice **Write the word from the box above that matches each definition below.**

1. _quite_ very

2. _shouted_ to call loudly

3. _tight_ held firmly

4. _flower_ a colored blossom

Apply Read each sentence. Then read the definition. See if the underlined word in the sentence matches the definition. Circle *Yes* or *No*.

5. Emma planted the <u>flower</u> seeds in a pot she made at school.
held firmly, secure . . . . Yes No

6. We will have to go <u>quite</u> soon.
very . . . . Yes No

7. My brother <u>shouted</u>, "It's time to eat!"
to call loudly . . . . Yes No

8. The football player kept a <u>tight</u> hold on the ball.
know . . . . Yes No

Name _____ **Date** _____

Explaining a Process

Think

Audience: **Who** will read your writing?

Possible Answer my teacher

_____

Purpose: **What** do you want your writing to do?

Possible Answer explain something to teach someone

Prewriting **Use the sequence map to plan and organize your ideas.**

First

| **Possible Answer** Dig a hole. |

Next

| **Possible Answer** Put the seeds in the hole. |

Then

| **Possible Answer** Put water in the hole. |

Last

| **Possible Answer** Cover the hole with soil. |

Revising Use this checklist to make your writing better.

☐ Are all the steps in the right order?

☐ Does each step have a time and order word?

☐ Is your title clear?

Editing/Proofreading Use this checklist to check your writing.

☐ Did you begin every sentence with a capital letter?

☐ Did you use correct end marks?

☐ Are all words spelled correctly?

Publishing Use this checklist to get your writing ready to share.

☐ Copy your writing on a clean sheet of paper.

☐ Draw a picture or find a photo to go with each step.

Name _____ **Date** _____

Selection Vocabulary

Focus

shrub (shrub) *n.* a bush (page 205)

vine (vīn) *n.* a plant that has a very long stem; can grow along the ground or up a wall (page 205)

stems (stemz) *n.* plural of **stem**: the stalk of a flower (page 211)

energy (e´•nər•jə) *n.* the strength to do something (page 219)

Practice **Match each word on the left to its definition on the right.**

1. shrub

2. energy

3. vine

4. stems

a. plural of stem; the stalk of a flower

b. a plant that has a very long stem

c. a small tree or bush

d. the strength to do something

Apply **Circle the correct word that completes the sentence.**

5. Mom went outside to water the _____.

   a. shrub **b.** sleep **c.** little

6. There were four flowers with four long _____ in the vase.

   a. stems **b.** energy **c.** jump

7. Alex saw a _____ growing up the trunk of a very tall tree.

   a. five **b.** open **c.** vine

8. We get _____ from the food we eat.

   a. think **b.** energy **c.** quite

Name _____ **Date** _____

Synonyms

Rule

Synonyms are words that mean the same or almost the same as other words.

Examples

look ⟶ see
like ⟶ enjoy

Practice **Read each sentence. Write a synonym for the underlined word.**

1. Tanzer is a <u>large</u> black cat.

   big

2. He <u>jumps</u> up when he sees a butterfly.

   leaps

3. Tanzer tries to <u>grab</u> it.

   catch

leaps

big

catch

Apply Read each word on the cat dish or fish. Write a synonym for the word on the line below the picture.

grab   crunchy   sack
hurry   under   beautiful

1.
bag

sack

2.
take

grab

3.
pretty

beautiful

4.
below

under

5.
crispy

crunchy

6.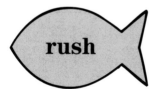
rush

hurry

Name _____ Date _____

Review Long and Short *o*

Practice Write the word that names the picture. Then write two more words that rhyme with that word.

| rope   toast   mop   sock |

1.
mop
hop
pop

2.
rope
hope
scope

3.
toast
coast
most

4.
sock
clock
rock

Apply **Read the riddle. Write the word that correctly answers the riddle. You will not use all of the words.**

office   doll   phone   frog   poem   fox   bolt   yo-yo

1.
I am an animal.
I live in the forest.
I belong to the dog family.
What am I?

fox

2. I can be long or short.
I am made up of words.
You can write me.
You can read me.
What am I?

poem

3. I have many meanings.
I can be a lot of fabric.
I can be a flash of lightning.
I can hold things together.
What am I?

bolt

4. I am in your home.
You can hold me.
I have buttons you push.
You use me to talk to people.
What am I?

phone

5.
I am a toy.
I have a string attached to me.
I go up, down, and around.
What am I?

yo-yo

6. I am a place to work.
I have a desk.
I am a room.
I have supplies.
What am I?

office

Name _____ **Date** _____

Classify and Categorize

Focus As you read, **classify and categorize** by grouping together things and ideas that are alike to help you better understand the selection.

Practice Read the category names in the box. Then read the words in each list. Write the name of the category that best describes the list of words. You will not use all of the names.

> Containers Sports Sounds Plants Tools

1. **Plants**
   tree
   fern
   bush
   flower

2. **Sports**
   football
   ice skating
   soccer
   softball

Apply   **Read each category. Choose words from the box that belong in each group. Write the words on the lines.**

> sandals   cracker   foil   book   stove   newspaper
> knife   carrot   food   gold   socks   pencil

3. Things to Read

book

newspaper

4. Sharp Things

knife

pencil

5. Crunchy Things

cracker

carrot

6. Things for Your Feet

sandals

socks

7. Shiny Things

foil

gold

8. In the Kitchen

stove

food

Name _____   **Date** _____

/ō/ spelled o_e and oa_

Focus

Rule	Examples
Long vowels sound like their names. Two ways /ō/ can be spelled are o_e and oa_.	dome robe boat road

Practice **Sort the spelling words under the correct heading.**

/ō/ spelled o_e

1. home
2. rope
3. stove
4. code

/ō/ spelled oa_

5. toad
6. coast
7. roam
8. goat

Word List
1. home
2. rope
3. toad
4. coast
5. stove
6. roam
7. goat
8. code

Challenge Words
9. lonely
10. cloak

Apply **Write a spelling word on the line that rhymes with each word.**

9. foam   roam

10. dome   home

11. load   toad

12. moat   goat

Write the spelling word next to its meaning clue.

13. a cord or line   rope

14. land next to the sea   coast

15. a system of symbols or letters   code

16. used for cooking or heating   stove

Name _____ Date _____

Writing a Summary

Think Audience: **Who** will read your summary?

Possible Answer my classmates

Purpose: **What** do you want your summary to do?

Possible Answer tell about a story I've read

Prewriting **Use the story map to plan your summary.**

Beginning:	**Possible Answer** Flowers are part of some plants.

Middle:	**Possible Answer** Flowers come from buds.

End:	**Possible Answer** People and animals use flowers.

Revising Use this checklist to make your summary better.

☐ Did you include the most important ideas?

☐ Did you make some sentences longer?

☐ Did you write the title and author's name at the top of your paper?

Editing/Proofreading Use this checklist to check your summary.

☐ Did you begin every sentence with a capital letter?

☐ Did you begin the title and author's name with capital letters?

☐ Did you use correct end marks?

Publishing Use this checklist to get your summary ready to share.

☐ Copy your summary on a clean sheet of paper.

☐ Draw a picture to go with your summary.

Name _____ **Date** _____

Antonyms

Focus

Rule
Antonyms are words that mean the opposite or nearly the opposite of another word.

Example
in ⟶ out

Practice **Read each word. Choose an antonym from the box that goes with the word. Write it on the line.**

found   rude   dull   shut

1. sharp ___dull___

2. open ___shut___

3. lost ___found___

4. polite ___rude___

Apply **Read each sentence. Write the antonym for the underlined word.**

> cool   short   light   down

1. It was a <u>warm</u> summer day.

   cool

2. My family went for a <u>long</u> hike.

   short

3. We hiked <u>up</u> a rough trail.

   down

4. Each of us carried a <u>heavy</u> backpack.

   light

Name _____ **Date** _____

Sounds and Spellings Review

Practice **Write the word from the word box that means almost the same thing as the word next to each number.**

| smudge | human | stumble |
| shrub | cube | crunch |

1. tumble   stumble   2. bush   shrub

3. smear   smudge   4. chew   crunch

5. block   cube   6. person   human

Apply   Read the sentences and circle the words with the short u or long u sound. Write each word under the correct column at the bottom of the page.

It was time for (lunch) (Huey) was (hungry) He looked at a (menu) and ordered a (sub) sandwich. When the sub came, it was (huge)

short u

lunch

hungry

sub

long u

Huey

menu

huge

Name _____ Date _____

Compare and Contrast

Focus To help you better understand as you read, **compare and contrast** ideas, characters, and events.

Practice Read the words in the box. Choose words that describe only a carrot and only celery. Then write the words that describe both.

> vegetable   grows above ground   grows under ground
> healthy   green   crunchy   orange   grows from seeds

Carrot

orange

grows under ground

Celery

grows above ground

green

Both

vegetable   healthy

crunchy   grow from seeds

Apply   **Read the story. Choose words from the box that describe each pet. Then write words that describe both.**

> girl   eight weeks old   short brown hair
> long white hair   playful   boy   puppies

Ben just brought home two new pets. They are both eight-weeks old. They love to play with Ben. Cosmo is a boy. He has short brown hair. Sassy is a girl. She has long white hair.

Cosmo

short brown hair

boy

Sassy

girl

long white hair

Both

eight weeks old   puppies

playful

Name _____ **Date** _____

Long u spelled *u* and *u_e*

Focus

Rule	Examples
Long vowels sound like their names. Two ways long u can be spelled are **u** and **u_e**.	uniform tube

Practice **Sort the spelling words under the correct heading.**

Word List
1. human
2. unit
3. fuel
4. music
5. mute
6. cube
7. huge
8. fumes

Challenge Words
9. unite
10. amuse

long u spelled *u*

1. human
2. unit
3. fuel
4. music

long u spelled *u_e*

5. mute
6. cube
7. huge
8. fumes

Apply   Circle the correct spelling for each word. Write the correct spelling on the line.

9. (music)   moosic   music

10. unet   (unit)   unit

11. fuems   (fumes)   fumes

12. muet   (mute)   mute

Write the spelling word next to its meaning clue.

13. great size   huge

14. used to produce heat or power   fuel

15. a solid shape with six equal sides   cube

16. a person   human

Name _____ **Date** _____

Selection Vocabulary

Focus

petals (pet´•əl)
n. Plural of
petal: colored leaves
of a plant (page 235)

bright (brīt) *adj.*
colorful (page 250)

Practice **Write the word from the word box that completes each sentence.**

1. The _____**bright**_____ flowers grew
in pots outside the store.

2. Roses have pretty _____**petals**_____ .

3. The _____**petals**_____ of the
daisy are long and white.

4. An artist used many _____**bright**_____ paints to make
that picture.

Apply Review the vocabulary words and definitions from "Flowers" and "Flowers at Night." Write a sentence using each vocabulary word.

> bright   petals

5. **Possible Answer** The sun was bright when we walked to the park.

6. **Possible Answer** The rose has pretty red petals.

Name _____ **Date** _____

Writing a Summary

Think **Audience: Who** will read your summary?

Possible Answer my teacher

_____

Purpose: What do you want your summary to do?

Possible Answer show my teacher what I learned

Prewriting **Use the web to plan your summary.**

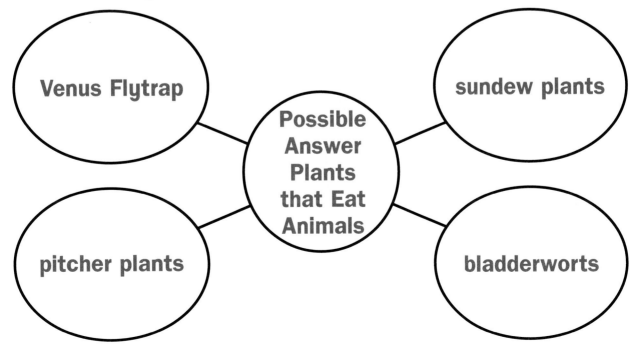

Revising   **Use this checklist to make your summary better.**

☐ Did you include the most important ideas?

☐ Did you write sentences of different lengths?

☐ Did you include contractions when appropriate?

Editing/Proofreading   **Use this checklist to check your summary.**

☐ Did you begin the title and author's name with capital letters?

☐ Did you use correct end marks?

☐ Are all words spelled correctly?

Publishing   **Use this checklist to get your summary ready to share.**

☐ Copy your summary on a clean sheet of paper.

☐ Make a poster or book jacket to go with your summary.

Name _____ **Date** _____

Selection Vocabulary

Focus

trapping (trap´•ing) *v.* allowing entrance but no exit (page 260)

wetlands (wet´•landz) *n.* land consisting of marshes and swamps (page 261)

attracts (ə•trakts´) *v.* draws attention to (page 262)

insects (in´•sekts) *n.* Plural of **insect:** a six-legged bug with a three-part body and no backbone (page 262)

Practice **Write the vocabulary word that completes each sentence.**

1. Many animals make their home in _____wetlands_____.

2. Some plants can get food by _____trapping_____ bugs.

3. The sweet smell of roses _____attracts_____ bees.

4. _____Insects_____ sometimes are eaten by plants.

Apply Write the word from the word box that matches each definition below.

| trapping   wetlands   attracts   insects |

5. _wetlands_ marshes and swamps

6. _insects_ a bug with six legs

7. _trapping_ allowing entrance but no exit

8. _attracts_ draws attention to

Name _____ Date _____

Contractions

Focus

Rule

A **contraction** puts two words together. Some letters are left out. An apostrophe (') shows where the letters are missing.

Examples

do not ⟶ **don't**

you will ⟶ **you'll**

Practice On the skateboard, write the contraction for the two words above the wheels.

I'm   doesn't   it's   they'll   we're

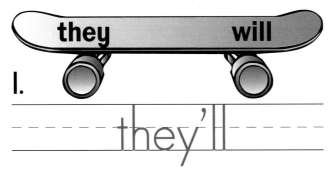

1. they   will

they'll

2. I   am

I'm

3. we   are

we're

4. it   is

it's

Apply **Read each sentence. Write the contraction for the underlined words.**

5. <u>It is</u> such a hot day. It's

6. Dad said <u>he will</u> barbecue. he'll

7. He <u>can not</u> find his cooking tools. can't

8. Look, <u>they are</u> in a box on the shelf. they're

9. The burgers <u>will not</u> get burnt. won't

10. <u>You are</u> a great cook, Dad! You're

Name _____ **Date** _____

Sounds and Spellings Review

Practice **Read the sentence. Rewrite the sentence using a word that means the opposite of each underlined word.**

| open | tame | follows | tiny | likes | night | stays |

1. Rudy is a large wild cat.

   Rudy is a tiny tame cat.

2. Rudy hates closed doors.

   Rudy likes open doors.

3. He leads me to his food dish every morning.

   He follows me to his food dish every night.

4. Rudy leaves when we have visitors.

   Rudy stays when we have visitors.

Apply **Read the clue. Write the word in the puzzle.**

reuse   telescope   grinder
cider   music   California

Across

1. To use again

3. A state on the west side of the United States

Down

2. A tool to help see far away

3. A drink made from apples

4. Sounds that make a tune, or notes on a page

5. A tool that chops food

Name _____   **Date** _____

/ī/ spelled _ie
/ō/ spelled _ow

Focus

Rule	Examples
Long vowels sound like their names. /ī/ can be spelled _ie. /ō/ can be spelled _ow.	fried bow

Word List
1. tie
2. grow
3. low
4. cried
5. pie
6. throw
7. lie
8. know

Challenge Words
9. window
10. dried

Practice Sort the spelling words under the correct heading.

/ī/ spelled _ie

1. tie
2. cried
3. pie
4. lie

/ō/ spelled _ow

5. grow
6. low
7. throw
8. know

Apply Below each word, write the spelling words that rhyme.

die

9. _tie_

10. _pie_

11. _lie_

fried

12. _cried_

row

13. _grow_

14. _low_

15. _throw_

16. _know_

Look at each word below. Write the spelling word that is part of the same word family.

17. tied _____ tie

18. throws _____ throw

19. pies _____ pie

20. knows _____ know

Name _____ **Date** _____

Writing a Report

Think | Audience: **Who** will read your report?
Possible Answer my teacher, my parents

Purpose: **What** do you want your report to do?
Possible Answer Give information or facts about something.

Prewriting | **Write your topic in the center of the word web. Gather facts about that topic and write the facts on the word lines.**

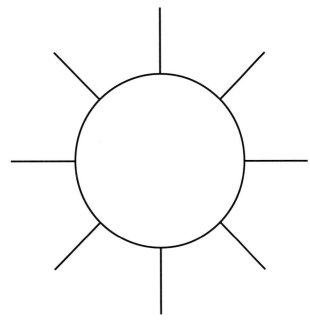

Revising Use this checklist to revise your report.

☐ Have you included all the facts from your word web?

☐ Did you use proofreading marks to make revising easier?

☐ Did you add details to your report to make it better?

☐ Did you delete information that does not belong?

Editing/Proofreading Use this checklist to correct mistakes.

☐ Have you used the present and past tense of verbs correctly?

☐ Are all words spelled correctly?

☐ Did you revise your report with a partner?

Publishing Use this checklist to get your report ready to share.

☐ Copy your report on a clean sheet of paper or write it on the computer. Give your report a title.

Name _____ **Date** _____

Present and Past Tense Verbs

Focus **Verbs** show action. You add *—ed* to a verb to show that something has already happened.

Practice **Read each sentence. Circle the verb. Then draw an X on the line under the correct column to tell if the verb is present or past tense.**

	Present	Past
1. Dad (enjoyed) our soccer game last week.	_____	X
2. Polar bears (play) in the water.	X	_____
3. Yesterday we (wrapped) gifts for grandpa.	_____	X
4. Chad (sprinkles) glitter on his picture.	X	_____
5. Aunt Mia (cooks) great waffles.	X	_____
6. Mom (dressed) the baby in warm clothes.	_____	X

Apply Read each sentence. Circle the correct verb and write it on the line.

1. Travis ___worked___ hard to finish his model airplane.

   work (worked)

2. Yesterday, Dana ___planted___ many seeds in her garden.

   plants (planted)

3. The bunny ___hopped___ out of its pen last night.

   hops (hopped)

4. The neighbors ___painted___ their house last month.

   paint (painted)

5. They always ___listen___ to the soccer coach before the game. (listen) listened

6. The people ___clapped___ when the show was over.

   clap (clapped)

Name _____ Date _____

Sounds and Spellings Review

Practice Read each word. Write the word in the correct column to tell if the e has the long or short sound.

> sleepy   tread   reason
> meter   speckled   heading

Short e

1. tread

2. speckled

3. heading

Long e

1. sleepy

2. reason

3. meter

Apply **Read the story. Write the correct word to complete each sentence.**

fell	cheered	season	speedy	even	loudly
team	field	pep	fence	bench	ended

This was the last game for the __season__.

Our __team__ sat on the __bench__

in the dugout. Coach Greer gave us a

__pep__ talk. The game was almost over and the score was

__even__. Then Steven hit the ball over the __fence__.

It __fell__ in the __field__. Steven was

__speedy__ and made a home run. The game

__ended__! We jumped up and down

and __cheered__ __loudly__.

Name _____ **Date** _____

Selection Vocabulary

Focus

packed (pakt) *adj.* filled tightly (page 22)

clay (klā) *n.* soft, sticky mud (page 24)

roof (roof) *n.* the outer covering of the top of a house or building (page 23)

sturdy (stûr´•dē) *adj.* strong (page 22)

Practice **Write the word from the word box that completes each sentence.**

1. Some bricks are made of ____clay____.

2. The ____roof____ of the house kept out the rain.

3. Sticks and ____packed____ mud can make a strong house.

4. The cat climbed up the ____sturdy____ tree.

Apply **Draw a line to match each word on the left to its definition on the right.**

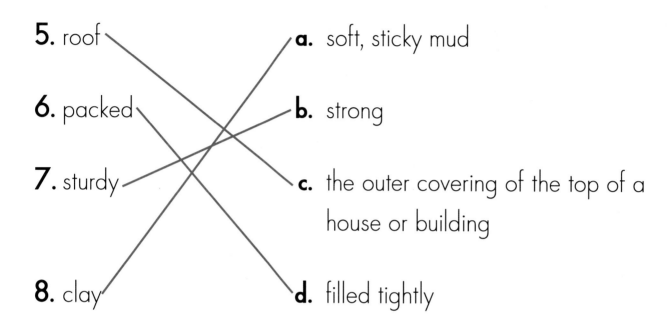

5. roof

6. packed

7. sturdy

8. clay

a. soft, sticky mud

b. strong

c. the outer covering of the top of a house or building

d. filled tightly

Name _____ **Date** _____

/ē/ spelled *ea* and *ee*

Focus

Rule	Example
Long vowels sound like their names. Two ways /ē/ can be spelled are **ea** and **ee.**	d**ea**l m**ee**t

Practice **Sort the spelling words under the correct heading.**

Word List
1. bead
2. seal
3. feet
4. greet
5. bee
6. tree
7. leak
8. flea

Challenge Words
9. teacup
10. meeting

/ē/ spelled *ea*

1. bead
2. seal
3. leak
4. flea

/ē/ spelled *ee*

5. feet
6. greet
7. bee
8. tree

Apply **Write the spelling word next to its meaning clue.**

9. a wingless insect

flea

10. an insect that gathers nectar and pollen

bee

11. to welcome in a friendly way

greet

12. to close up something

seal

Look at each word below. If the word is spelled correctly, write the word *correct* on the line. If the word is misspelled, write the correct spelling on the line.

13. trea

tree

14. leak

correct

15. fet

feet

16. beed

bead

Name _____ **Date** _____

Irregular Past Tense Verbs and Past Tense Verbs Ending in *y*

Focus

Rule	Examples
• Some spellings of verbs change to show that something has already happened. Those verbs do not use an *–ed*.	We **sing** the song today. We **sang** the song yesterday.
• Verbs that end with a *y* change when you add an *–ed*. The *y* changes into an *i* and the *–ed* is added.	Katie tries to **hurry.** Katie **hurried** to catch the bus.

Practice   **Read each sentence. Circle the verb. Then draw an X under the correct column to tell if the verb is present or past tense.**

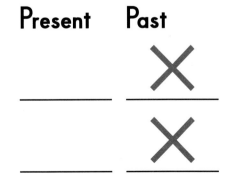

Present   Past

1. My sweater (shrank) in the dryer.   _____   X

2. Chuck (studied) hard for his math test.   _____   X

Read each sentence. Circle the correct word and write it on the line.

3. Dad _____lit_____ the campfire an hour ago.

   lights   (lit)   lighted

4. Yesterday, Margo _copied_ her paper neatly.

   copies   copy   (copied)

5. Missy _came_ to school late yesterday.

   comes   come   (came)

6. The play _began_ an hour ago.

   begins   (began)   beginning

7. Dad and Ted _dried_ the dishes last night.

   (dried)   dry   drying

8. We _bought_ new sneakers last weekend.

   buy   (bought)   buying

Name _____ Date _____

Sounds and Spellings Review

Practice Read each sentence. Circle the word with the blend. Write the blend on the line at the end of the sentence.

1. The puppy curled up in the soft (blanket.)   bl

2. We (celebrated) our team's victory.   br

3. Anna (promised) to be on time.   pr

4. A tiny (muskrat) dashed under the bush.   sk

5. We walked up the (crooked) path.   cr

6. She only had time to (glance) at the newspaper.   gl

7. We bought red (flowers.)   fl

Apply   **Read the story. Write the word that correctly completes each sentence.**

> stopped   froze   snow
> grasped   streets   slowly

Last night was so cold that ice _froze_ on the

streets. Patty and Jake walked _slowly_ down

the _snow_ covered sidewalk. They reached the bus stop

just as the school bus _stopped_. They _grasped_ the

handlebar as they got on the bus.

Name _____ **Date** _____

Selection Vocabulary

porch (pôrch) *n.* an entrance covered with a roof (page 44)

cement (si•ment´) *n.* a mix of sand, water, and rock that dries as hard as stone (page 53)

electrician (i•lek•trish´•ən) *n.* a person who works with wires and electricity (page 56)

hut (hut) *n.* a small plain house (page 40)

Practice **Review the vocabulary words and definitions from *Building a House* and *Homes Around the World*. Write two sentences using at least one of the vocabulary words in each sentence.**

1. _____
   _____

2. _____
   _____

Apply **Write the word from the word box that matches each definition below.**

> hut   porch
> electrician cement

1. porch : an entrance covered with a roof

2. electrician : a person who works with wires and electricity

3. hut : a small plain house

4. cement : a mix of sand, water, and rock that dries as hard as stone

Name _____ **Date** _____

Consonant Blends /st/ and /tr/

Focus

Rule
- Consonant blends join two or more consonants with little change in the individual sounds. Listen carefully for the individual sounds.
- The consonant blend /st/ is spelled **st** and the consonant blend /tr/ is spelled **tr.**

Example
st ore   tr ade

Word List
1. stamp
2. stick
3. steal
4. stay
5. true
6. train
7. track
8. try

Challenge Words
9. stable
10. truly

Practice Sort the spelling words under the correct heading.

/st/ spelled *st*

1. stamp
2. stick
3. steal
4. stay

/tr/ spelled *tr*

5. true
6. train
7. track
8. try

Apply Look at each word below. If the word is spelled correctly, write the word *correct* on the line. If the word is misspelled, write the correct spelling on the line.

9. smick stick

10. track correct

11. frue true

12. smay stay

13. steal correct

14. try correct

15. prack track

16. frain train

Write the spelling word on the line next to its meaning clue.

17. take without permission steal

18. not false true

19. course or path track

20. to walk heavily or noisily stamp

Name _____ **Date** _____

Putting Titles in Alphabetical Order

Focus It is helpful to organize your books in **alphabetical order** when you are doing research. You can organize books by arranging the selections in ABC order, using the first word of the title. If there are several titles that start with the same word, then also look at the second word in the title.

Practice **Read the book titles and then write them on the lines in alphabetical order.**

How a Seed Grows   Plant that Eat Animals

Green and Growing   Flowers

Flowers

Green and Growing

How a Seed Grows

Plant that Eat Animals

Apply Write the titles from the Home Sweet Home Unit in alphabetical order.

Snail's Pace   The White House   Building a House

Homes   Homes Around the World

Building a House

Homes

Homes Around the World

Snail's Pace

The White House

Name _____ **Date** _____

Classify and Categorize

Focus **Classify and Categorize:** As you read, group together things and ideas that are alike.

Practice Read each category. Write the words on the lines under the category in which they belong.

library	fairy tales	doorknob
office	fables	clock

Kinds of Books

fables

fairy tales

Rooms in a School

library

office

Things That are Round

clock

doorknob

Apply Read each list. Write the category that best describes the words on the list.

Summer Clothes   In a Grocery Store
Desert Animals   Happy Things
Winter Clothes   In a Garage
Pet Care

In a Garage

garden hose

spare tires

ladder

car

Desert Animals

rattlesnake

scorpion

tarantula

camel

Clothes

shorts

tee shirts

swimsuit

sandals

Pet Care

fresh water

food

keep safe

hugs

Name _____ **Date** _____

Explaining a Process

Think **Audience: Who** will read your explanation?
Possible Answer my teacher, my friend

Purpose: What do you want your explanation to do?
Possible Answer Tell the reader how to do something.

Prewriting **Complete the sequence map below to help you plan your writing. Use one of the topics from your Writer's Notebooks.**

My Topic To My Room

First Come in the front door.	**Next** Walk straight back.
And then Turn left down the hall.	**Finally** Walk in my room.

Revising **Use this checklist to revise your writing about a process.**

☐ Is your first step at the beginning?

☐ Did you turn each idea into a complete sentence?

☐ Are the steps clear and easy to follow?

☐ Did you move around text that might be out of place in the paragraph?

Editing/Proofreading **Use this checklist to correct mistakes.**

☐ Did you use proofreading marks to help make editing easier?

☐ Are all words spelled correctly?

☐ Did you have a partner read over your writing?

Publishing **Use this checklist to get your writing ready to share.**

☐ Copy your writing on a clean sheet of paper or write it on the computer.

☐ Give your writing a title at the top of the page.

Name _____ **Date** _____

Future Tense Verbs

Focus

Rule
Future tense verbs show an action that will happen in the future. It can be formed by using the word *will* with the verb.

Example
I **will finish** my homework tonight.

Practice

Read each sentence. Draw a line under the future tense verb.

1. Soon they will load the boxes on the truck.

2. We will walk to school tomorrow.

3. Maria will make treats for our picnic next Saturday.

4. Our team will play a game this weekend.

5. The cat will climb up that tree.

6. I will go on a trip.

Apply Read each sentence. Circle the words that will make it future tense and write them on the line.

7. Christy's family __will go__ camping next month.

 (will go) went

8. Dad __will pack__ everything the night before they leave. (will pack) packed.

9. Mom and Aunt Betty will prepare the food ahead of time.   prepared (will prepare)

10. Christy and Mark __will plan__ the games to take on the trip. (will plan) planned

11. Mark will hope his cousin will be there.

 hoped (will hope)

12. Their dogs Swaggerty and Callie will travel with them.

 (will travel) traveled

Name _____ **Date** _____

Sounds and Spellings Review

Focus Digraphs are two or more letters that make one sound.

Practice **Read each sentence. Circle the word with the digraph. Write the digraph on the line.**

1. We ate (brunch) at a new restaurant.

2. Dad put milk into a (pitcher.)

3. Bart made a (chart) about space travel.

4. Melinda used clay to (shape) a bowl.

5. We picked (fresh) strawberries out of our garden.

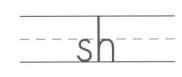

6. Mom and I put family (photos) in a new album.

Apply Read each riddle. Write the correct word on the line.

cheese   alphabet   sunshine   clothing

7. I make words.
I have vowels and
consonants.
I have 26 letters.
What am I?

alphabet

8. I am food.
I can be yellow or white.
Mice really like me.
What am I?

cheese

9. You wear me.
I am a shirt.
I am a robe.
What am I?

clothing

10. You see me a lot in the
summer.
You play out in me.
I come from the sun.
What am I?

sunshine

Name _____ Date _____

Main Idea and Details

Focus Good readers identify the **main idea** and **details** of a selection to help them better understand what is happening.

Practice **Read the main idea and the details. Then circle the sentence that does not belong.**

Main Idea: Weather

Details:

1. The snow was melting in the sunshine.

2. It was so cold that the rain turned into hail.

3. They went swimming in the pool because it was so hot.

4. He had to take a bath because he was covered with dirt.

5. The cool air outside made her nose cold.

6 His mom drove him to school because it was raining.

Apply **Read the main idea. Then circle the words that do not belong.**

Main Idea: Materials used to make shelters

Details:

wood	dirt	(grapes)
leaves	cement	mud
bricks	nails	cloth
(water)	sticks	ice
reeds	stones	(birds)

Name _____ **Date** _____

Consonant digraphs /sh/ and /ch/

Focus

Rule

- Consonant digraphs are consonants next to each other that represent one sound. The sound can be at the beginning or end of a word or syllable.
- The consonant digraph /sh/ is spelled *sh* and the consonant digraph /ch/ can be spelled *ch* or ■ *tch*.

Example

shop   bun**ch**

Word List

1. ship
2. rich
3. shade
4. teach
5. chalk
6. dish
7. wash
8. check

Challenge Words

9. shadow
10. child

Practice Sort the spelling words under the correct heading.

/sh/ spelled *sh*.

1. ship
2. shade
3. dish
4. wish

/ch/ spelled *ch*.

5. rich
6. teach
7. chalk
8. check

Apply **Read each word. If the word is spelled correctly, write *correct* on the line. If the word is misspelled, write the correct spelling.**

9. shalk   chalk

10. rish   rich

11. ship   correct

12. teash   teach

13. shade   correct

14. dish   correct

15. sheck   check

16. wach   wash

Write the spelling word next to its meaning clue.

17. to look over   check

18. used for marking   chalk

19. a large vessel for water travel   ship

20. shallow container for holding food   dish

21. wealthy   rich

22. blocking of light rays   shade

Name _____ Date _____

Organizing Story Sequence

Writing a **story sequence** is like making a map that shows information from a reading selection. Organizing a story sequence can also help you plan something you are going to write.

Practice **Read each sentence below. Number them in the order they would come in a story.**

__4__ First we got out some board games to play.

__6__ Finally, the sun came out.

__1__ It was a rainy day.

__5__ Then we colored pictures with crayons and markers.

__2__ We could not play outside.

__7__ We put on our jackets and ran through the door.

__3__ We decided to play inside.

Apply **The story below is written in the wrong order. Read the story and rewrite the sentences so they are in the correct order.**

My dad put on the training wheels. It was time to practice riding my bike. I practiced riding up and down the sidewalk. My dad cheered as I took off riding on just two wheels. Then it was time for Dad to take off the training wheels.

It was time to practice riding my bike. My dad put on the training wheels. I practiced riding up and down the sidewalk. Then it was time for Dad to take off the training wheels. My dad cheered as I took off riding on just two wheels.

Name _____ **Date** _____

Selection Vocabulary

Focus

trudge (truj) *v.* to walk slowly with heavy steps (page 82)

famous (fā´•məs) *adj.* well known (page 77)

president (prez´•i•dənt) *n.* the leader of the United States (page 67)

Practice **Write the word from the word box that completes each sentence.**

I. Bill had to _____trudge_____ through deep snow to get to school.

2. The _____president_____ lives and works in the White House.

3. The Golden Gate Bridge is a _____famous_____ bridge.

Apply **Tell whether the boldface definition that is given for the underlined word in each sentence below makes sense. Circle Yes or No.**

trudge   famous   president

4. The <u>president</u> greeted visitors in the East Room.
watching   Yes   (No)

5. Dave had to <u>trudge</u> up the stairs with the heavy box.
sitting   Yes   (No)

6. Have you read about the most <u>famous</u> home in America?
well known   (Yes)   No

Name _____ **Date** _____

Timed Writing

Think **Audience: Who** will read your timed writing?
Possible Answer my teacher

Purpose: What do you want your timed writing to do?
Possible Answer Tell how animals in hot countries get shelter from the weather.

Prewriting **Follow these steps for timed writing.**

1. Read the entire prompt. Circle the directions for writing the paper.
2. Underline each thing you are asked to write about.
3. Reread each reminder.
4. Make notes about what you will write. Spend only a few minutes.
5. Write your paper!
6. Check to make sure you did each reminder.
7. Revise as needed.

Revising

Use this checklist to make your timed writing better.

☐ Did you complete each reminder?

☐ Does your writing stay on topic?

☐ Are your sentences clear?

Editing/Proofreading

Use this checklist to check your timed writing.

☐ Did you begin every sentence with a capital letter?

☐ Did you use correct end marks?

☐ Are all words spelled correctly?

Name _____ **Date** _____

Singular, Plural, and Possessive Nouns

Focus	Rule	Example
	Add **'s** to a noun or name to show ownership.	Jake**'s** hat the dog**'s** tail

Practice A **Read each sentence. Draw a line under the singular nouns. Circle the plural nouns. Draw a box around the possessive nouns.**

1. The (kittens) slept on the <u>chair</u>.

2. <u>Janet</u> put the (dishes) in the <u>sink</u>.

3. [Burt's] <u>horse</u> galloped to the <u>gate</u>.

Practice B **Read the sentence. Circle the correct word and write it on the line.**

1. The ___dog's___ water dish tipped over.

   dog (dog's) dogs

Singular, Plural, and Possessive Pronouns

Focus	Rule	Example
	A **possessive pronoun** takes the place of a possessive noun. It shows ownership.	Tammy's shoes are black. **Her** shoes are black.

Practice A Read each sentence. Draw a line under the singular pronouns. Circle the plural pronouns. Draw a box around the possessive pronouns.

1. Jessie and I raked their leaves.

2. We played the big drums in the parade.

Practice B Rewrite the sentence to change the underlined nouns to pronouns.

3. Kathy's book is in Mike's desk.
Her book is in his desk.

Name _____ Date _____

Sounds and Spellings Review

Practice A Read each category. Write the words that belong under each category.

snarl	drummer	burro	storyteller
horns	partridge	slurp	teacher

People

storyteller

teacher

Sounds

snarl

slurp

A Parade

drummer

horns

Animals

burro

partridge

Practice B

swirled   shore   surrounded   storm

There would not be a ___storm___ at the coast today. We

walked along the sandy ___shore___. Cool little waves

___swirled___ around our feet. We laughed as the seagulls

___surrounded___ the breadcrumbs that we tossed on the sand.

Name _____ **Date** _____

Compare and Contrast

Focus You will better understand and keep track of what you read if you identify things within the selection that are **alike** and **different.**

Practice A **Compare and contrast a car and a pickup truck. Tell how each is different. Then tell how they are alike.**

seatbelts	open in back	shorter

 Car

Truck

shorter _____ open in back

A car and a truck are alike.

seatbelts

Practice B **Read each description. At the bottom, tell how the objects are different and how they are alike.**

Crayons are made of wax. Crayons come in many colors. You can use a crayon to draw a picture.

Pencils are made of wood. Pencils make black marks. They have erasers so you can correct mistakes. You hold a pencil in your hand. You can use a pencil to draw a picture.

Crayon	Alike	Pencil
wax	hold in hand	wood
many colors	use to draw a picture	black marks
		has an eraser

Name _____ **Date** _____

R-controlled Vowels

Focus

Rule	Example
R-controlled vowels make a special sound. The r-controlled vowel sound /ar/ spelling is **ar** and the r-controlled vowel sound /or/ spelling is **or.**	m**ar**k w**or**n

Word List

1. park
2. cart
3. order
4. core
5. store
6. torn
7. hard
8. harm

Challenge Words

9. garden
10. story

Practice A **Sort the spelling words under the correct heading.**

/ar/ spelled *ar*

1. park
2. cart
3. hard
4. harm

/or/ spelled *or*

5. order
6. core
7. store
8. torn

Practice B

Beside each word, write the spelling word that rhymes on the line.

9. yard   hard

10. more   store

11. start   cart

12. farm   harm

13. worn   torn

14. border   order

15. dark   park

16. sore   core

Spelling • *Skills Practice 2*

Name _____ Date _____

Selection Vocabulary

Focus

creatures
(krē´•chərz) *n.*
Plural of **creature:**
a living person or
animal (page 91)
hibernating
(hī´•bər•nāt´•ing)
v. Form of the verb
hibernate: to sleep
through the winter
(page 94)

shady (shā´•dē) *adj.*
giving shade; blocking
out light (page 96)
comfort (kum´•fərt)
n. a good feeling;
having what you need
(page 110)

Practice A   **Write the word from the word box
that completes each sentence.**

1. The bear left the den after <u>hibernating</u> for many weeks.

2. Dan found a <u>shady</u> spot in the yard.

3. We came in from the cold to enjoy the __comfort__ of a warm room.

4. Many __creatures__ in the desert are active at night.

Practice B   **Write the word from the word box that matches each definition below.**

hibernating	shady
comfort	creatures

5. __shady__ blocking out light

6. __creatures__ living people or animals

7. __hibernating__ sleeping through the winter

8. __comfort__ a good feeling; having what you need

Name _____ Date _____

Writing an Opinion Statement

Think Audience: **Who** will read your statement?
Possible Answer my parents, my classmates

Purpose: **What** do you want your opinion statement to do?
Possible Answer Tell what I think and feel about a topic.

Prewriting **Complete the web below to help get ideas for your opinion statement. Remember to focus on the question:** *Which kind of house would be more fun to live in, a tree house or a house boat?*

Can fish for food		On water
	House boat	
It floats		Can swim

Revising **Use this checklist to revise your opinion statement.**

☐ Does every sentence tell about your opinion on the question?

☐ Did you add descriptive details and re-write unclear sentences in your sentences?

☐ Did you explain your opinion to a partner to come up with ideas for your writing?

Editing/Proofreading **Use this checklist to correct mistakes.**

☐ Did you choose the correct tense for the verbs in your writing?

☐ Did you edit your writing with a partner to help find your mistakes?

Publishing **Use this checklist to get your report ready to share.**

☐ Copy your opinion statement on a clean sheet of paper.

Name _____ **Date** _____

Selection Vocabulary

Focus

tunnels (tun´•əlz) *n.* Plural of **tunnel:** an underground passageway (page 123)

shared (shârd) *v.* Past tense of **share:** to divide with others (page 135)

Practice A **Circle the correct word that completes the sentence.**

I. The ants lived in sandy _____ under the grass.

   a. different   **b.** turning   **c.** tunnels

2. My brother and I _____ a room for two years.

   a. shady   **b.** shared   **c.** storm

Practice B Review the vocabulary words and definitions from *This House Is Made of Mud.* Write two sentences using at least one of the vocabulary words in each sentence.

1. Answers will vary. Accept complete sentences that use at
2. least one vocabulary word.

Name _____ **Date** _____

Past, Present, and Future Verbs Review

Practice A **Read each sentence. Circle the verb. Then write an X under the correct column to tell if the verb is the past, present, or future tense.**

	Past	Present	Future
1. Lindsey (giggles) at everyone's jokes.		X	
2. We (spent) hours washing the car.	X		
3. Bob and Jim (will play) soccer next spring.			X
4. The playful kittens (pounce) on each other.		X	
5. Laura (will play) the piano this summer.			X
6. Ryan (rides) the bus to day camp.		X	

Practice B **Read each sentence. Circle the verb that correctly completes each sentence and write it on the line.**

7. I am _going_ to the dentist tomorrow.

   go   (going)   gone

8. Mr. Dalmane will _make_ new toys for next year.

   (make)   making   made

9. Julian _returned_ the books to the library last week.

   return   returning   (returned)

10. Sharon _jumps_ rope all recess.

    (jumps)   jumping   jumped

11. Last night the wind _blew_ very hard.

    blows   blowing   (blew)

12. Brad and Marv are _helping_ dad clean out the garage.

    help   (helping)   helped

Name _____ Date _____

Sounds and Spellings Review

Name each picture clue. Write the word in the puzzle.

| cartwheel | sweatshirt | toothbrush | pitcher |
| melon | tractor | thermometer | grapes |

Across

1.
3.
4.
5.

Down

1.
2.
6.
7.

Across: 1. t r a c t o r
3. m e l o n 4. g r a p e s
5. s w e a t s h i r t

Down: 1. toothbrush 2. thermometer 6. cartwheel 7. pitcher

Sounds and Spellings Review

Write the missing word to complete each sentence.

8. We ate bread and honey for __breakfast__.

   (breakfast)   butter

9. He laid a __heavy__ carpet over the hard floor.

   cloudy   (heavy)

10. Mr. Davis went to the __airport__ to pick up my grandfather.

   airplane   (airport)

11. Steven __whistled__ for his dog Cosmo to come.

   (whistled)   rang

12. Trisha stacked three __cartons__ on the shelf.

   cartoons   (cartons)

13. Tyler dug a bigger hole in the __dirt__ before he added more seeds.

   (dirt)   down

Name _____ Date _____

Making Inferences

Focus **Making Inferences** is using what you already know to help answer questions while reading.

Practice A **Read the paragraph. Read the questions. Draw an X on the line in front of the correct answer. Then follow the directions.**

The bell rang. All of us quickly put our pencils and papers in our desks. We listened for our row to be called. Then we quietly put on our jackets and lined up at the room door. We walked down the hallway and out the doors. The air felt a little chilly. A few of us hurried to the swings. Others ran to the slides. Some just started chasing each other.

I. Where are the children?

_____ at summer camp   ✗_____ at school

Draw a line under the words in the paragraph that tell you this.

Using the story from page 183, answer the questions below. Draw an X on the line in front of the correct answer. Then follow the directions.

2. What time of year is it?

_____ hot summer

$\times$ fall

Circle the words in the paragraph that tell you this.

3. What are the children doing?

$\times$ having recess

_____ eating lunch

Draw a box around the words that tell you this.

Name _____ **Date** _____

Consonant Digraphs /hw/ and /th/

Focus

Rule
Consonant digraphs are two consonants next to each other that represent one sound.
The consonant digraph /hw/ is spelled **wh** and the consonant digraph /th/ is spelled **th.**

Example
what   **th**ick

Word List
1. path
2. three
3. birth
4. white
5. whale
6. throw
7. whim
8. while

Challenge Words
9. whistle
10. thought

Practice A

Sort the spelling words under the correct heading.

/hw/ spelled *wh*

1. white
2. whale
3. whim
4. while

/th/ spelled *th*

5. path
6. three
7. birth
8. throw

Practice B   **Beside each word, write the spelling word that rhymes.**

9. kite   white

10. mirth   birth

11. show   throw

12. sale   whale

Write the spelling word next to its meaning clue.

13. a sudden idea or impulse   whim

14. a track or trail   path

15. a period of time   while

16. a number   three

Name _____ **Date** _____

Persuasive Writing

Think Audience: **Who** will read your persuasive poster? **Possible Answer** my teacher, my friends

Purpose: **What** do you want your persuasive poster about fear to do? **Possible Answer** Tell about being afraid and how to deal with your fears.

Prewriting **Brainstorm ideas to use for your poster below.**

1. What things are you afraid of?

Possible Answers dogs, spiders, roller coasters

2. What are some ways that you can overcome your fears?

Possible Answers I can talk with someone about my fears.

On another sheet of paper draw a picture of what your poster might look like.

Revising **Use this checklist to make your poster better.**

☐ Does your poster help readers want to think, feel or do something about facing a fear?

☐ Does your poster tell about what you are afraid of and how you can deal with that fear?

Editing/Proofreading **Use this checklist to correct mistakes.**

☐ Did you begin every sentence with a capital letter?

☐ Did you use correct end marks?

☐ Are all words spelled correctly?

Publishing **Use this checklist to get your persuasive poster ready to share.**

☐ Did you add a picture or photo to your poster?

☐ Does your poster have a title?

Name _____ Date _____

Adjectives, Synonyms, and Antonyms

Focus

Rule	Examples
Adjectives are describing words that tell more about something.	bright brighter brightest

Practice A Read each sentence. Circle the adjective. Write an X on the line to tell if it compares two or more than two.

	Compares 2	Compares More Than 2
1. Chad is the (fastest) runner on our team.		X
2. The blue rope is (longer) than the red one.	X	
3. This cracker is the (crunchiest) I ever ate.		X
4. Mrs. Garcia's oak tree is (older) than ours.	X	

Practice B **Read the word pairs. Write S if they mean the same. Write O if they mean the opposite.**

5. subtract   add   O

6. fix   repair   S

7. plump   fat   S

8. healthy   sick   O

9. full   empty   O

Read each sentence. Circle the word that correctly completes the sentence. Write the word on the line.

10. Carla keeps her bedroom neat and _tidy_.

(tidy)   messy

11. The puppy is not strong enough to walk on its weak baby legs.

powerful   (weak)

Name _____ **Date** _____

Sounds and Spellings Review

Practice A Unscramble the letters and write the word on the line. Find and circle the word in the puzzle.

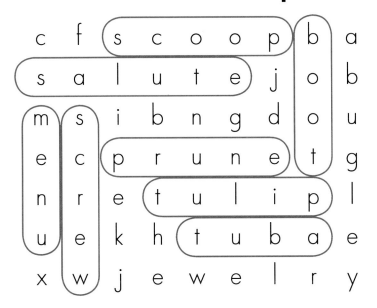

1. c w e s r   screw   2. n u r p e   prune

3. a u t b   tuba   4. a u t e s   salute

5. n m u e   menu   6. p u i t l   tulip

7. o b o t   boot   8. o s p c o   scoop

Sounds and Spellings Review

Practice B **Look at the picture. Read each sentence. Write the word that rhymes with the underlined word and makes sense to complete each sentence.**

| stew | mule | spoon | brook | goose |

9. It is no <u>use</u> to try to catch that <u>goose</u>.

10. He can play a <u>tune</u> with a <u>spoon</u>.

11. The <u>rule</u> is to keep the <u>mule</u> in the pen.

12. Is it <u>true</u> dad makes a great <u>stew</u>?

13. <u>Look</u> at all the fish in the <u>brook</u>!

Name _____ Date _____

Vocabulary

Focus

underneath (un´ • dər • nēth´) *adv.* below (page 150)

beards (bērdz) *n.* Plural of **beard:** the hair that grows on a man's face (page 151)

clenched (klencht) *v.* Past tense of **clench:** to close tightly (page 166)

trembling (trem´ • bəl • ing) *v.* shaking (page 166)

Practice A **Write the word from the word box that completes each sentence.**

1. Maria clenched her fist around her lunch money.

2. Jeff tried to look brave, but his hands were trembling.

3. Our dog took my shoe underneath my bed to chew it.

4. Many presidents of the United States wore beards.

Practice B **Write the word from the word box that matches each definition below.**

> underneath   trembling
> beards   clenched

5. <u>beards</u> the hair that grows on a man's face

6. <u>clenched</u> to close tightly

7. <u>underneath</u> below

8. <u>trembling</u> shaking

Name _____ **Date** _____

/o͞o/ spelled oo and /oo/ spelled oo

Focus

Rule	Examples
The short /oo/ spelling is oo. One spelling for long /o͞o/ is oo.	m**oo**d t**oo**k

Word List

1. droop
2. book
3. good
4. noon
5. moose
6. food
7. shook
8. wood

Challenge Words

9. balloon
10. wooden

Practice A **Sort the spelling words and write them under the correct heading.**

/o͞o/ spelled oo

1. droop
2. noon
3. moose
4. food

/oo/ spelled oo

5. book
6. good
7. shook
8. wood

Practice B **Beside each compound word, write the spelling word that it contains.**

9. cookbook   book

10. good-bye   good

11. firewood   wood

12. seafood   food

Write the spelling word next to its meaning clue.

13. middle of the day   noon

14. to bend or hang down   droop

15. material from trees   wood

16. a hoofed mammal   moose

Name _____ **Date** _____

Alphabetical Order

Focus Fiction books are placed on shelves in **alphabetical order**. The librarian places these books on shelves according to the author's last name. The first letter of the author's last name is used in alphabetical order.

Practice A Underline the first letter of the author's last name. Put these letters in alphabetical order at the bottom of the page.

Allan <u>F</u>owler

Chieri <u>U</u>egaki

Arnold <u>L</u>obel

Lois <u>O</u>sborn

Deborah <u>E</u>aton

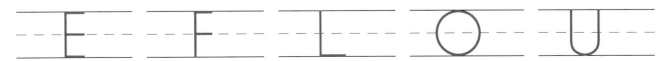

E   F   L   O   U

Practice B **Write the author's names on the lines in alphabetical order.**

Margaret Clark

Bernard Waber

Marc Brown

Robin Nelson

Joan Sweeney

Marc Brown

Margaret Clark

Robin Nelson

Joan Sweeney

Bernard Waber

Study Skills • *Skills Practice 2*

Name _____ **Date** _____

Drawing Conclusions

Focus Readers **draw conclusions** by taking small pieces of information about a character or story event and use the information to guess something about the character or event.

Practice A **Look at each picture. Then answer each question. Circle your answers.**

1. How does Christy feel?

   a. sad   (**b.** proud)

2. Why does she feel this way?

   (**a.** She grew the biggest pumpkin.)

   b. The judge is smiling.

   c. She is at the fair.

Practice B **Read the story. Answer each question with an X. Follow the directions under each question.**

Pam (rubbed her hands) while looking up and down the street. She (pulled her coat around her) and (put her hands in her pockets.) Sitting on the bench, Pam (shivered) and waited.

3. Where is Pam?   inside _____   outside _____

Draw a line under the words in the story that tell you this.

4. What is it like outside?   cold _____   warm _____

Draw circles around the words in the story that tell you this.

Name _____ **Date** _____

Writing a Summary

Think Audience: **Who** will read your summary?
Possible Answer my teacher,
my mom and dad

Purpose: **Why** is it important to be able to write a summary?
It tells the most important ideas
from a selection or story.

Prewriting **Plan your summary by completing the outline below.**

Main Characters: a girl, a dog, bugs, a mom

List two important things that happen in the story.
• the girl was afraid of things
• the girl hid under her covers

How did the story end?
• The girl decided not to miss out on things anymore by hiding.

Revising **Use this list to help make your summary better.**

☐ Do the sentences of your summary have different lengths so that they do not all sound the same?

☐ Does your summary have a beginning, a middle, and an end?

☐ Did you remember to include the story's title and author at the top of the summary?

Editing/Proofreading **Use this checklist to correct mistakes in your summary.**

☐ Did you use capital letters and end marks correctly?

☐ Are all words spelled correctly?

Publishing **Use this checklist to get your summary ready to share.**

☐ Copy your summary on a clean sheet of paper.

Name _____ **Date** _____

Types of Sentences

Focus **Telling sentences** tell a thought and end with a period. **Asking sentences** ask a question and end with a question mark.

Practice A **Draw a line under the telling sentences. Circle the asking sentences.**

1. Which one can we go on first?

2. I want to ride on the brown horse.

3. Do you think Bill can hit the target?

4. I had a fun day at the park.

Types of Sentences

Focus **Strong-feeling** sentences show surprise or excitement and end with an exclamation point. **Imperative** sentences give a command and can end with a period or exclamation point.

Practice A

Write two strong feeling sentences about the picture.

Answers will vary. Possible answers may include:

I love your dog!

Wow, you have a big dog!

Write command sentences about the picture.

Answers will vary. Possible answers may include:

Stop, Max!

Hold on to the leash tightly.

Name _____ Date _____

Sounds and Spellings Review

Practice A Read the headings. Write the words under the category where they belong.

growl	browse	owl	towel	shout	hound
pouch	pounce	howl	point	oyster	soil

Animals

owl

hound

oyster

Sounds

growl

shout

howl

Things You Can Do

browse

pounce

point

Things You Can Hold

towel

pouch

soil

Practice B **Write the correct word to complete the sentences in the story.**

crown town loud crowd gown loyal tower

The queen heard __loud__ cheers. She put on her purple

velvet __gown__ and jeweled __crown__.

She went to look out a window in the __tower__.

Below she saw a large __crowd__. The people of the

__town__ would always be __loyal__ to her.

Name _____ Date _____

Diphthongs /ow/ spelled *ou_* and /oi/ spelled *oi*

Focus

Rule	Example
The /ow/ sound can be spelled *ou_*, and the /oi/sound can be spelled *oi*. The /ow/ and /oi/ sounds are made by making a gradual movement from one vowel sound to the next vowel sound.	ro**u**nd co**i**l

Word List

1. sound
2. couch
3. boil
4. house
5. soil
6. loud
7. coin
8. noise

Challenge Words

9. around
10. joined

Practice A Sort the spelling words under the correct heading.

/ow/ spelled *ou_*

1. sound
2. couch
3. house
4. loud

/oi/ spelled *oi*

5. boil
6. soil
7. coin
8. noise

Practice B Circle the correct spelling for each word. Write the correct spelling on the line.

9. soind (sound) _____ sound

10. (boil) boyl _____ boil

11. (coin) coyn _____ coin

12. howse (house) _____ house

Write the spelling word that rhymes with each word.

13. coil _____ soil

14. pouch _____ couch

15. cloud _____ loud

16. poise _____ noise

Name _____ **Date** _____

Organizing Story Sequence

Focus **Organizing a story's sequence** is a way to map what has happened in a story. A story sequence, or outline, can also be used to help you plan something you are going to write.

Practice A **Write sentences that describe action in the last story we read, "My Brother Is Afraid of Just About Everything." You may refer back to *Student Reader 2* to review details from the story.**

Answers will vary. Accept sentences that describe what happened in "My Brother Is Afraid of Just About Everything."

_____

_____

_____

Practice B **Create a story sequence by writing the sentences from the story in the correct order.**

1. Answers will vary. Sentences
2. must be written in the order
3. they occurred in the story.

4. _____

5. _____

6. _____

7. _____

8. _____

Name _____ **Date** _____

Vocabulary

Focus

thrill (thril) *n.* a feeling of excitement (page 189)

peeking (pēk´ • ing) *v.* looking quickly or secretly (page 203)

solo (sō´ • lō) *n.* music that one person sings or plays on an instrument (page 191)

sneaking (snēk´ • ing) *v.* moving or acting quietly, secretly (page 203)

Practice A **Write the word from the word box that matches each definition below.**

| peeking | solo |
| thrill | sneaking |

1. peeking — looking quickly or secretly

2. thrill — a feeling of excitement

3. <u>sneaking</u> ------- moving or acting quietly, secretly

4. <u>solo</u> _____ music that one person sings or plays

on an instrument

Practice B **Circle the correct word that completes the sentence.**

5. We heard Lee play a _____ on his flute.

  a. hen   (**b.** solo)   **c.** walking

6. Dad and I were _____ into the crib to see the sleeping baby.

  (**a.** peeking)   **b.** solo   **c.** weekend

7. My mom enjoys the _____ of riding a roller coaster.

  a. voice   **b.** cute   (**c.** thrill)

8. A cat was _____ past the door without a sound.

  (**a.** sneaking)   **b.** flower   **c.** smooth

Name _____ **Date** _____

Writing a Fable

Think

Audience: **Who** will read your fable?
Possible Answer my friends, a brother or sister

Purpose: **What** do you want your fable to do?
Possible Answer Tell a story that teaches a lesson.

Prewriting **Use the story map to plan your fable.**

Beginning
Possible Answer There were two foxes who were friends, Jerry and Larry.

Middle
Possible Answer Jerry took some berries from Larry and ate them. The berries made Jerry sick.

End **Possible Answer** They weren't berries to eat. The juice from the berries was for painting a picture. Jerry learned he should not take things that don't belong to him.

Revising — Use this checklist to make your fable better.

☐ Does your fable have a title?

☐ Does your fable have talking animals?

☐ Is there a problem in your fable that is solved in the end?

☐ Does your fable have a moral or teach a lesson?

Editing/Proofreading — Use this checklist to check your fable.

☐ Did you begin every sentence with a capital letter and end it with the correct end mark?

☐ Are all words spelled correctly?

☐ Did you have a peer edit your fable?

Publishing — Use this checklist to get your fable ready to publish.

☐ Copy your fable on a clean sheet of paper or type it on the computer.

☐ Draw an illustration to go with your fable.

Name _____ Date _____

Reality and Fantasy

Focus In **reality stories,** characters talk and act like real people, and the events could happen in real life. In **fantasy stories,** the main characters are often animals that talk and behave like people. Fantasy stories could never happen in real life.

Practice A **Read each sentence below. If it is an example of reality, write *reality* on the line. If it is an example of fantasy, write *fantasy* on the line.**

1. Bob the beaver asked his friend Tom the tuna to help him build a home for his family.

2. Jill wanted a new sweater. She asked her mom if she could earn money by doing extra chores.

Practice B Circle **Reality** or **Fantasy.**

3. Eddie and Sam put up the tent.   (Reality)   Fantasy

4. Leo Leopard yelled, "I'm going to jog to the park."   Reality   (Fantasy)

5. The pig carefully drove the tractor to the cornfield.   Reality   (Fantasy)

6. Rusty walks his dog Dusty every day.   (Reality)   Fantasy

7. Wanda Wolf read a bedtime story to her cubs.   Reality   (Fantasy)

8. Rachel helped Mom fold the clean clothes.   (Reality)   Fantasy

Name _____ **Date** _____

Capitalization

Focus **Rule**

Use a **capital letter** for the first word of a sentence, the pronoun I, cities and states, names of special people, places, and things, days of the week, and the months.

Practice A **Read each sentence. Draw a line under the words that should begin with a capital letter. Write the correct capital letter above the word.**

    M   M   S
1. <u>miguel</u> lives in <u>madrid</u>, <u>spain</u>.

    H   J
2. <u>his</u> family will visit us in <u>june</u>.

    I   S   O
3. <u>it</u> is a long trip to <u>seaside</u>, <u>oregon</u>.

    W   S L C
4. <u>we</u> want to show them the <u>sea</u> <u>lion</u> <u>caves</u>.

Read each sentence.
Write the sentence
correctly on the line.

5. the new portsmouth zoo opened the first monday in july.

The new Portsmouth Zoo opened the first Monday in July.

6. my family and i want to see the baby pandas.

My family and I want to see the baby pandas.

7. our friends mrs. selvin and paula will go with us.

Our friends Mrs. Selvin and Paula will go with us.

Name _____ Date _____

Word Building

Practice A Read each word.
Circle the base word.
Draw a line under the prefix and/
or word ending.

1. (blushed)

2. (smarter)

3. (darting)

4. (quietness)

5. (higher)

6. dis(appear)

7. un(feeling)

8. (chores)

9. un(true)

10. (pecking)

11. (weeded)

12. dis(infect)ed

13. (plainness)

14. un(finish)ed

FINISH

Practice B Read each sentence. Write the correct prefix or word ending to complete the word.

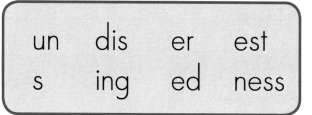

un	dis	er	est
s	ing	ed	ness

15. Kim zoom___ed___ out the door.

16. Mom was ___dis___pleased that the puppy had chew___ed___ the mat.

17. Nan was ___un___afraid of exploring the cave.

18. Mr. Chin was water___ing___ his flower___s___.

19. The thick___ness___ of the jacket made it too bulky.

20. Jane writes the neat___est___ papers in the class.

21. Kayla can do math problems quick___er___ than Steven.

22. Mr. Bailey ___un___lock___ed___ the door.

Name _____ **Date** _____

Vocabulary

usually
(ū´•zhoo•əl•ē)
adv. most of the time
(page 211)

clumsy (klum´•zē) *adj.*
awkward; not graceful
(page 213)

suggest (səg•jest´) *v.*
to give or tell an idea
(page 227)

excitement
(ik•sīt´•mənt) *n.* a
mood or feeling of high
interest or energy;
delight; joy (page 228)

Practice A **Match each word on the left to
its definition on the right.**

1. suggest

2. usually

3. excitement

4. clumsy

a. awkward, not graceful

b. a mood or feeling of high
interest or energy; delight; joy

c. to give or tell an idea

d. most of the time

Practice B **Tell whether the boldface definition that is given for the underlined word in each sentence below makes sense. Circle Yes or No.**

1. I am going to <u>suggest</u> we go for a walk after dinner.
quickly   Yes   (No)

2. Emily <u>usually</u> rides the bus to go downtown.
never   Yes   (No)

3. Rico decided to practice skating so he would not feel <u>clumsy</u> on the ice.
awkward   (Yes)   No

4. The <u>excitement</u> of the birthday party lasted all afternoon.
feeling of high energy   No

Name _____ **Date** _____

Word Endings –s and –ed

Focus

Rules	Examples
• The common ending spelled **–s** means more than one or an action that is happening right now.	The cat sit**s**. The other cat**s** run.
• The common ending spelled **–ed** means that something has already happened. It can make the /ed/ sound, /d/ sound, or /t/ sound.	end**ed** color**ed** bak**ed**

Word List
1. likes
2. liked
3. opens
4. opened
5. parts
6. parted
7. chases
8. chased

Challenge Words
9. buried
10. exclaimed

Practice A

Sort the spelling words and write them under the correct heading.

ending spelled -s

1. likes
2. opens
3. parts
4. chases

ending spelled -ed

5. liked
6. opened
7. parted
8. chased

Practice B Look at each word below. If the word is spelled correctly, write the word *correct* on the line. If the word is misspelled, write the correct spelling on the line.

9. chasez   chases   13. partd   parted

10. opend   opened   14. likd   liked

11. likes   correct   15. partes   parts

12. chased   correct

Write the spelling words that complete each word family.

16. like   liked   likes

17. part   parted   parts

18. open   opened   opens

19. chase   chased   chases

Name _____ Date _____

Alphabetical Order

It is helpful to organize your books in **alphabetical order** when you are doing research. Then, it is easy to find the title you are looking for without having to remember the author's name.

Practice A Underline the first word in each of the book titles. Then put the books in alphabetical order.

Suki's Kimono   _Red-Eyed Tree Frog_

Back to School   _Zinnia's Flower Garden_

1. _Back to School_
2. _Red-Eyed Tree Frog_
3. _Suki's Kimono_
4. _Zinnia's Flower Garden_

Practice B **Write the title of four books from your classroom in alphabetical order.**

I. _____

2. _____

3. _____

4. _____

Answers will vary depending on the classroom library and the book choices students make. Check to see that students have listed the books in alphabetical order by book title.

Name _____ **Date** _____

Writing a Realistic Story

Think

Audience: **Who** will read your story?
Possible Answer my friends, the teacher

Purpose: **What** do you want your story to do?
Tell about something that could happen, but really didn't happen.

Prewriting

Use the story map to plan your story.

Beginning Possible Answer The main character is Laura. She wanted to go swimming with her friends. She could not find her swimsuit.

Middle **Possible Answer** Her friend Annie helped her look for it.

End **Possible Answer** Laura found her swimsuit. Laura and Annie went swimming.

Revising   **Use this checklist to make your story better.**

☐ Does your story have a title?

☐ Does your story tell about a problem and how it was solved?

☐ Does your story use describing words and action words?

Editing/Proofreading   **Use this checklist to check your story.**

☐ Did you begin every sentence with a capital letter and end it with the correct end mark?

☐ Are all words spelled correctly?

☐ Did you write contractions correctly in your story?

Publishing   **Use this checklist to get your story ready to publish.**

☐ Copy your story on a clean sheet of paper or write it on the computer.

Name _____ **Date** _____

Selection Vocabulary

Focus

problem (prob´ • ləm) *n.* a difficulty; a tricky or uncomfortable situation (page 239)

match (mach) *n.* a contest or game (page 244)

changed mind (chānjd mīnd) *v.* Past tense of **change mind:** to go back on a decision (page 262)

Practice A   **Review the vocabulary words and definitions from *Ira Sleeps Over.***

Write two sentences using at least one of the vocabulary words in each sentence.   **Answers will vary.**

1. Katie knew the answer to the math problem.

2. Niles passed the ball well during his soccer match.

Write the word from the word box that completes each sentence.

problem	match	changed mind

1. At first Nick wanted to play outside, but then he

   __changed__ his __mind__.

2. The icy roads caused a __problem__ for the drivers.

3. Ira and his friend had a wrestling __match__.

Name _____ **Date** _____

Contractions

Focus   A **contraction** is when two words are combined to make one word.

Practice A   **Write the contraction on the line. Use an apostrophe (') to show where letters are missing.**

I. I am   I'm

2. was not   wasn't

3. she is   she's

4. you will   you'll

5. we have   we've

Practice B

Read each sentence. Circle the two words that can make a contraction. Write the contraction on the line.

6. (I am) going to camp soon.

7. Mark said (he is) going also.

8. (It is) going to be hot there.

9. (We will) need to pack shorts.

10. (I had) better start packing.

11. (They have) planned many fun things for us to do.

12. (We are) going to have fun!

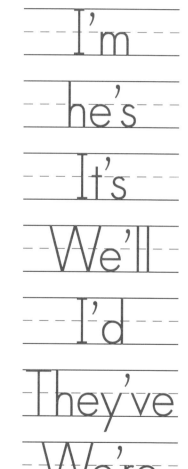

I'm

he's

It's

We'll

I'd

They've

We're

Name _____ **Date** _____

Sounds and Spellings Review

Write the correct word in the puzzle that names each picture.

| tray | robot | honey | rainbow |
| night | flute | window | money |

Across

3.

4.

6.

8.

Down

1.

2.

5.

7.

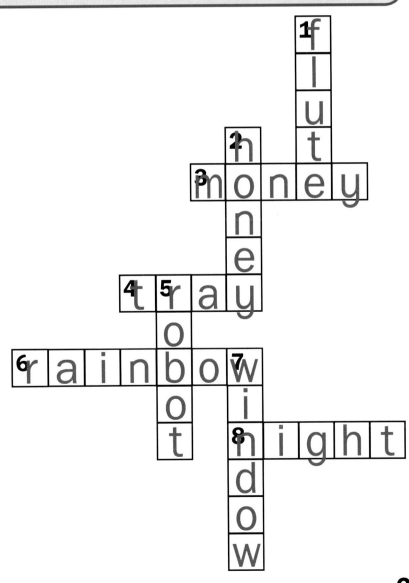

Sounds and Spellings Review

Read the sentences. Circle the words with long vowel sounds. Write them under the correct letter sound.

1. Sam drew nine names out of the huge jar.

2. Grandma can weave a rug.

3. Many cars travel along this road.

Aa

names

Ee

weave

Ii

nine

Oo

road

Uu

huge

Name _____ Date _____

Main Idea and Details

Focus Good readers stop to identify the **main idea and details** of the story to help them better understand what is happening.

Practice A **Read the main idea. Then circle the sentence that does not belong.**

Main Idea: Trying new things can be exciting.

1. I wanted to learn how to ride a two-wheel bike.

2. My aunt took me to the store to buy a bike helmet.

3. I was afraid I might fall off.

4. Cats can be friendly animals.

5. I was brave when I started peddling.

6. It was exciting when I took off by myself!

Skills Practice 2 • Comprehension

Main Idea and Details

Read the main idea. Then circle the words that do not belong.

Main Idea: Going to summer camp is fun.

Details:

cabins   (tigers)   (elephant)

trees   hiking   campfire

singing   friends   crafts

(lobster) counselors games

swimming boats   (whale)

Name _____   **Date** _____

Word Ending –ing

Focus

Rule
The ending spelled **–ing** is added when the base word ends in a consonant. If the base word ends in the letter e, the letter e is dropped before adding the ending spelled –ing.

Examples
walk → walk**ing**
ride → rid**ing**

Word List

1. pointing
2. looking
3. hoping
4. walking
5. biking
6. chasing
7. hiding
8. eating

Challenge Words

9. shrinking
10. hearing

Practice A   Sort the spelling words and write them under the correct heading.

ending spelled –ing

1. pointing
2. looking
3. walking
4. eating

ending spelled –ing after dropping final e

5. hoping
6. biking
7. chasing
8. hiding

Practice B Look at each word below. Write the spelling word that is in the same word family on the line.

9. chase

10. eat

11. point

12. hide

13. walk

14. look

15. hope

16. bike

chasing

eating

pointing

hiding

walking

looking

hoping

biking